Archie
Hero in Training

Sam Hay

MACMILLAN CHILDREN'S BOOKS

First published 2011 by Macmillan Children's Books
a division of Macmillan Publishers Limited
20 New Wharf Road, London N1 9RR
Basingstoke and Oxford
Associated companies throughout the world
www.panmacmillan.com

ISBN 978-0-330-53792-6

1 3 5 7 9 8 6 4 2

A CIP catalogue record for this book is available from
the British Library.

Printed and bound by CPI Group (UK) Ltd, Croydon CR0 4YY

Contents

Archie . . . and Spirit

Kate could hear them calling her, but she couldn't leave. Not yet. She buried her face in the soft black fur one last time.

'I'll miss you, Spirit,' she whispered. 'I'll never forget you.'

The young dog rested his head softly on her shoulder as though, somehow, he too knew this was goodbye.

'Come on!' called Dad from the hall. 'You're going to be late for school!'

Kate still didn't move. She stroked Spirit's silky black ears. 'You'll be the best guide dog ever,' she whispered, 'I know you will, but I wish you didn't have to leave . . .' She felt the tears coming now, and with one final effort, she hugged Spirit close for a moment, then got up, and left, trying not to look back. Spirit tried to follow; he always followed Kate. But not today. Kate slipped quickly through the door, closing it softly behind her, leaving the dog for the last time. Today Spirit would leave Kate's life forever, to take the final steps on his journey to becoming a guide dog.

It was a journey that had started more than a year ago when he'd been born into a litter of pups, each with the same destiny; to make a difference – to become a guide dog and change a blind or partially sighted person's life forever. Now, after twelve months of love and care from Kate and her family, Spirit had finished his puppy training – the first part of his journey was over. Today he would leave to begin his harness training at the Guide Dog's centre.

Kate buttoned her coat and tried to hide her tears. She felt too grown-up to cry – especially in front of her two little brothers. 'It's not fair!' she said, her sadness turning momentarily to anger. 'Why does he have to go?!'

'Because that's how it is,' said her mum gently. 'You knew it was going to happen . . .' She paused to brush the tears from Kate's cheek. 'Spirit was born to be a guide dog. We've done our bit – his puppy training is finished now. He has to move on.'

'But I don't want him to go!' Kate hid her tears behind her hair. 'I love him,' she added softly, so only her mum could hear.

'We all do, Kate, none of us wants to say goodbye.' Her mum could feel her own eyes welling up. She swallowed back the tears; she had to stay strong for the kids. But it was true, Spirit, the gentle black-Lab cross-breed, with the soft fur and chocolate-brown eyes, had touched them all deeply. From that first sunny morning, when he'd arrived on their doorstep as a tiny six-week-old pup, he'd fitted in with their family straight away. Kim, Kate's mum, had secretly worried that he wouldn't. Until recently they'd had two family dogs of their own. Then one died, leaving the other – an old schnauzer called Barney. Kim had worried that a bouncy new pup might have been too much for Barney, but she was wrong. From the start Spirit seemed to understand that Barney was old. The pup was unusually gentle and quiet around him and as a result the pair quickly became friends. Spirit took to the children immediately too; following them around, playing with them. He was always gentle and always kind, especially with the youngest, Sean, who was barely four at the time. When the children went to bed, he would settle down quietly with their parents, snuggled close to Barney. But now all that was finished, over forever, and Barney looked as glum about it as the rest of the family.

'Try not to be sad,' said Kim, hugging her daughter. 'Remember how important Spirit is. How much of a difference he'll make to someone's life.'

Kate bit her lip. She knew that he was important, but it didn't help the way she felt – the ache in her stomach and the cloud of sadness that surrounded her. She picked up her school bag and was about to leave, when suddenly she stopped and looked back towards the kitchen door: 'One last cuddle?'

Her mum shook her head. 'Best not, Kate. It'll only make it harder. Go on now, off to school. It'll feel better soon, I promise.'

Kate nodded, but it was no good. The house

just wouldn't be the same without Spirit. For the past year he'd been everywhere with the family: shopping trips, days out, holidays. He loved a fast run in the park and playing on the beach in Wales. He loved chewing Kate's old slippers and dressing gown, and chasing his toys in the garden, and wrestling with her brother Mark.

The trouble was Spirit was a dream dog – the type every family wanted; quiet and gentle but full of fun, always eager to please, and at his happiest when he was close to humans.

It had been a family decision to have him. Kim had read about becoming a puppy walker for Guide Dogs, and instantly felt it was something she'd like to do. Puppy walkers are the people who look after guide dog puppies for the first year of their life. It's an important job; like laying the foundations of a building. Without strong foundations a building would fall down, and without good puppy training, no dog could hope to become a guide dog. There is so much for the pups to learn: from basic house training to strict obedience. The pups also have to be introduced to lots of new experiences: loud noise, cars, buses, children, crowds of people, other dogs, travelling, shops . . . so that by the time they reach the final stage of their training, nothing should phase them or distract them from doing their job.

Kim had felt ready to be a puppy walker. Her youngest son, Sean, was starting school soon so she would have the time necessary to give a pup the attention and training he or she would need. It wasn't a decision to take lightly, and the family discussed the idea for more than a year. Kim's husband, Paul, had grown up with dogs. He was an experienced owner; he knew

how to train a dog properly, but he also knew
how attached you became to a dog – even one
that isn't really yours. How would the children
cope with letting the pup go? Paul and Kim
explained this to Kate, then aged nine, and her
brother Mark, then seven. Both understood
the rules. They would have a new pup to play
with – but after a year, they'd have to give him
back. The children readily agreed; a year had
seemed so far off back then. Now, when that
day had suddenly arrived, they realized that
saying goodbye wasn't easy at all.

'We'll keep in touch with Spirit,' said Kate's
dad as he backed the car out of the drive, heading
for school. 'We'll find out how he gets on at
training.'

Kate nodded. She could picture him there.
When Spirit had been just a few months old
she'd actually visited the training centre with

her mum. She had wanted to see for herself what happened there and how they turned bouncy pups into real working dogs that made such a difference to their blind or partially sighted owners. She'd done a project all about it for school, explaining in detail everything she'd experienced. It had been a day she'd never forget. As soon as she'd arrived at the centre she'd been caught up in the world of guide dogs. The manager had taken her to meet – and cuddle – three tiny puppies in the breeding section. Then she'd gone on to the training section itself, where the older dogs were being put through their paces. She'd watched them escorting their owners carefully and confidently around complicated obstacle courses, around barriers, and bollards and trees . . . Then, to really show her what it was like, Kate had been allowed to experience it for herself. They blindfolded her and let one of the experienced dogs, Lennie, lead *her* around the course. It was frightening not to be able to see, to have to depend on someone else to keep you safe. It was hard to trust that the dog wouldn't let anything happen to her. But he didn't. Kate suddenly understood what a huge difference a guide dog must make to someone who can't see. She also realized that these dogs were not cuddly pets any more – they were working dogs, born to do a job. At the end of her visit, she was glad she could take off the blindfold. She left the centre with a new respect for guide dogs and the training they received. She felt proud that her family were part of it, but that didn't make it any easier to say goodbye to Spirit now.

They'd arrived at school. Kate wasn't crying any more. She managed to give her dad a small smile before she got out of the car and joined the crowd of children streaming through the school gates, but she still felt sad and a bit empty. She tried not to think about the end of the day, when she'd have to return home to a house without Spirit.

Weeks passed and Kim was right. The children adapted quickly. They missed Spirit, of course, but the empty feeling gradually faded. They had a holiday to look forward to. No one mentioned how much Spirit would have enjoyed the trip, even though inside they were all thinking it. There was something else the family was thinking of, but didn't talk about much – their new guide dog puppy. He would be arriving when they got back from holiday.

Kim was worried. It was the night before the pup was due to arrive and she was lying awake in bed, fretting. Was it a good idea to have another one? It wasn't just the children who missed Spirit, she did too. She didn't talk about it – she didn't want to make it worse for the children – but she thought about him often. After all, they had spent so much time together –while the children were at school and Paul was at work. She'd taken Spirit everywhere with her. She'd cared for him. She'd trained him. She remembered with a smile the day in the supermarket when he'd chewed the bottom of her shopping bag and all her groceries fell out and rolled away . . . Then there was the family barbecue, when Spirit just couldn't help himself and he'd pinched a sausage roll from under Sean's nose! Kim smiled; so many happy memories, which had made it all the harder to say goodbye. Could she bear to go through it all again? She wanted so much to be involved with Guide Dogs – to give something back and make a difference . . . Still unsure, she fell asleep, and then finally the day arrived, and it was too late to change her mind.

The children were excited – though Kate and Mark both vowed to themselves that they wouldn't let themselves get too close to the puppy this time. Even so, they headed off to school chatting about the pup, wondering what he'd be like. Kim was wondering too. She watched the clock, waiting for him to arrive. Then finally he did. Archie: a seven-week-old golden Lab-retriever cross. Not a bit like Spirit. Not black and silky, or gentle and quiet. Archie was small and round, a pale-yellow colour, with a mischievous twinkle in his eye. He was cautious at first – the house and its inhabitants were new to him – but for some reason Kim had the feeling that this little pup would be quite a handful!

She helped him settle in, showing him his new

bed and his toys and introducing him to Barney, who was thirteen now and almost blind. The old dog raised his head briefly to look at the new arrival, and then, unimpressed, went off to find a quiet corner to have a snooze.

The rest of the day passed quickly, then just after half past three the front door crashed open and the children arrived.

'Awww!' breathed Kate. 'He's gorgeous!' She gathered the little pup up in her arms and he happily responded, licking her cheeks and squealing with delight. Mark was next . . . 'Come on, boy!' he said, grabbing one of the pup's chewy toys, and soon they were having a very giggly session of tug-of-war on the floor. Sean was next, showering the pup with hugs and kisses. Eventually, exhausted, the pup conked out in his bed.

Much later, as Kim turned off the lights and

headed for bed herself, she felt a strange sense of calmness in the house. She was glad Archie was here; he'd already brought so much happiness with him and it was lovely to see the kids playing with a puppy again. Having him in their home was the right thing to do, she was sure of that now.

As she climbed into bed she listened out for a moment, and heard Archie whimpering. It was understandable. He was only a baby, and this was his first night away from his litter-mates. All across the country, his brothers and sisters would be settling down for their first night alone too. Kim put on her dressing gown and went down to check on him.

'Don't worry, Archie,' she said, stroking his small head softly. 'You'll be all right . . .'

And he was. After that first night, Archie settled in quickly and Kim's initial impression of the pup had been spot on. He was a lively little dog – full of fun and mischief. He wasn't at all sensitive to Barney's age and frequently bounded up to the old dog, wanting to play. He chewed anything he could find and liked nothing better than a bit of rough-and-tumble wrestling with Mark and Sean. He was a bit of a charmer too. Whenever the family took him out shopping he always attracted a lot of attention. Shop assistants, hairdressers, cafe staff – everyone would coo and fuss over Archie. He lapped up the attention! Kate and Mark, despite their promises to themselves, both fell for him fast, but, strangely, it felt different this time. Of course they'd miss him when eventually he had to leave – but they were ready for it this time. Archie was a guide dog puppy – and in a year he would leave: that was just how it had to be. And accepting that fact somehow made it easier.

★

Weeks turned quickly to months, and though Kim never stopped thinking about Spirit, her days were busy – training Archie. He had so much to learn, so many new situations to experience. Then one day she got a call. It was Spirit's new handler at the Guide Dogs training centre. Kim felt a knot in her stomach at the mention of Spirit's name. She took a deep breath and steadied herself against the wall as she listened while the handler told her all about how well Spirit was doing with his advanced training and what a brilliant job Kim and her family must have done during his puppy training. Kim beamed with pride. She still felt sad, but she also felt immensely proud – proud of Spirit and proud of what she and her family had achieved.

Just as she hung up, Archie zoomed past her with a cushion in his mouth, closely followed by

Kate, Mark and Sean. Kim grinned. It was hard to believe that Archie – that tiny golden bundle of fun who chewed their ankles and chased his toys around the garden – would one day soon be a real working dog too – a hero even; a dog that someone would rely on and trust to help them lead a more independent life . . . but then that was the magic worked by Guide Dogs and their army of dedicated trainers.

Arthur

It was the puppy's ears that Dawn noticed first. They were big and bat-like, almost too large for his head; it was as though he'd borrowed them from a much larger dog for the day and forgotten to give them back.

'Hello, Arthur,' said Dawn, bending down to pat him. 'Welcome to your new home.'

He glanced at her quickly and then looked away. She smiled. This was typical German-shepherd behaviour; slightly aloof, independent. German shepherds were complicated dogs. Unlike retrievers or Labradors, shepherds weren't always eager to please. They took their time, weighing up every situation to see whether it was worth their while bothering or not. Arthur was obviously still deciding.

Dawn watched as the pup padded around her home. This would be his home too for the next twelve months and Dawn would be his puppy walker, which meant she was responsible for the first stage of his guide dog training. She smiled as he sniffed and explored every corner. He was a handsome little chap. At six weeks old, he was already the size of a piglet. It was hard to believe he'd weighed less than a pack of butter when he'd been born just a few weeks ago.

As he trotted past her into the kitchen Dawn watched and wondered. Would he make it as a guide dog? It was hard to tell. Did he have the right qualities? She wasn't sure. It was difficult to know what sort of dog the pup would become. If he made it, Arthur could be the best of the best; German shepherds could make incredible guide dogs. With their intelligence, strength, stamina and unwavering loyalty some people thought of them as the Rolls-Royce of the guide dog world.

But as Dawn knew from experience, getting a shepherd through their training was fraught with problems. There were so many issues to overcome. For a start, German shepherds liked to be boss. Without a firm hand they could be disobedient or even bullies. They could be anxious dogs and unusual situations or strangers could scare them. Loyalty was another problem. When a shepherd bonded with its owner it was a bond for life. Dawn would need to keep a distance between her and Arthur, because if they got too close there was a real danger he wouldn't cope when he had to leave her. There were health concerns too. German shepherds often had problems with their hips and, because of their size, troubles could develop during growth spurts, making them lame or knock-kneed. Any, or all, of these problems could scupper Arthur's chances of becoming a guide dog and it was up to Dawn to somehow lead Arthur through the potential pitfalls and see him safely into his formal training.

'Well . . .' said her husband, Ian. 'What do you think of him then?' A farmer's lad himself, Ian was an experienced dog owner and he enjoyed helping Dawn with guide dog pups.

'He doesn't trust me yet,' she said, pausing as she heard a whimper from downstairs. 'He's still making up his mind . . .' She listened as another whimper came from below. This was Arthur's first night away from his brothers and sisters and Dawn had expected a bit of fuss from the little pup. Arthur was her fifth guide dog puppy and first nights were often difficult for the young dogs.

'I'll go and check on him,' she said. But just as she put one foot out of bed the whimpers suddenly stopped. Ian and Dawn sat in silence for a few minutes, listening. There was no more noise.

Ian smiled. 'A Lab wouldn't settle so quickly.'

'True,' she grinned. 'Arthur's a confident little character. He pretends he doesn't really need us. But we'll see . . .'

At two o'clock in the morning, Arthur *did* need Dawn, and at four o'clock and six o'clock too. He needed to go to the toilet. By her third visit downstairs Arthur was friendlier, though still wary. Earning his trust would clearly take time.

'Come on, Arthur, catch me if you can!' Eight-year-old Jude — a full-of-beans, tousle-haired lad — was playing on the swing at the bottom of Dawn's garden. Every time he swung backwards or forwards Arthur would leap into the air in an attempt to touch the boy's toes with his nose. The higher he swung, the higher the dog jumped — to whoops of delight from Jude.

Dawn and Jude's mum, Marie, were watching from the other end of the garden.

'He's taken a real shine to that pup!'

Dawn nodded. 'I thought he might have been a bit afraid of him, as Arthur is so big now, but that hasn't happened . . .'

She was right. When Jude had seen Arthur it had been love at first sight. He and his family were holidaying with Dawn for a few days, and since they'd arrived Jude and four-month-old Arthur had become inseparable. From first light to bedtime they were always together. Sometimes they would be playing with Arthur's much-loved miniature space-hopper toy (that squeaked when he squeezed its ears) and sometimes they would practise Arthur's puppy training – with Jude giving the commands and rewarding him with titbits when he did well. Most of the time the two friends would simply roll around on the grass together doing silly stuff.

'I'll never hear the end of it when we leave,' sighed Marie. 'He'll be asking for a dog of his own again – only this time, it'll have to be a German shepherd just like Arthur!' She smiled at her son. His face was flushed and glowing while Arthur leaped in the air like a mad March hare! If dogs could smile, thought Dawn, Arthur would be grinning from ear to ear.

Arthur loved children. When Dawn took him to the shopping centre for one of his puppy training trips, he would wag his tail at the mere sound of a child's voice. He liked to be close to them, he liked the smell of them and most of all he adored being fussed over by them. Of course parents were wary of him, as German shepherds have a reputation for being fierce, but the children often made a beeline for Arthur. Thankfully, when he was wearing his special guide dog lead adults could see what sort of dog he was training to become, so they softened and joined in the fuss. Strangers would stop Dawn in the street – they were so interested in the dogs, and so kind to them. This was one of the many reasons Dawn loved her job – it was a great way to meet people. It was helpful for the dogs too; the more experience they had of strangers and noise the better, because to be a good guide dog nothing should phase them. The guide dogs had to be able to cope in all situations, from heavy traffic to large crowds. So far Arthur was flying through his training. He'd learned to sit and wait, to respond to a whistle and to walk in the middle of the pavement without sniffing the ground searching for distractions. He'd even begun to get a little closer to Dawn. He was still aloof and independent, and Dawn felt he was constantly assessing her to see what he could get away with, but he liked a bit of a cuddle now and again too!

As Jude waved a tearful goodbye to Arthur, it looked like he was on track to pass on to his advance training at the Guide Dogs training centre. Then something happened, something that at the time seemed unimportant, but would have far-reaching consequences for Arthur and his chances of making it as a guide dog.

It was a few days after Jude's visit, and Arthur and Dawn were visiting friends nearby. Arthur loved it there; the family's gentle black

Labrador was a particular chum of his. The two dogs were playing happily in the garden. Nobody had noticed the family cat sunbathing in the shrubbery. Then, disaster . . . just as Arthur trotted past, the cat suddenly jumped to its feet beside him. The pup froze, the shock of the unexpected movement seeming to paralyse him. Then suddenly he took off, squealing, his tail between his legs, shaking and terrified. It was ridiculous really; almost cartoon-like. After all, Arthur was already a big dog – much bigger than the cat. But for some reason the shock of seeing it appear unexpectedly next to him had scared the pup senseless. Dawn found him cowering in the bushes and it was a while before he could be persuaded to come out.

From that day on Arthur disliked cats. He would bark loudly whenever he saw one. This behaviour wasn't at all acceptable for a guide dog, and it was a worry for Dawn — but there were other hurdles to overcome too.

Dawn had arranged to take Arthur to Devon for a holiday. It was a long way from their Scottish home and they would need to fly. Dawn knew the journey would be a good experience for the pup. When the airport tannoy announced that their plane was ready to board Arthur trotted confidently to the gate with Dawn. As he was a guide dog in training he and Dawn were allowed to get on the plane first and the crew had reserved a row of seats for them. Arthur settled quickly, lying calmly at Dawn's feet. This was more like it; this was what she'd expect from a guide dog in training. As the aeroplane taxied down the runway, ready for take-off, the captain made an announcement welcoming their 'special visitor'. Dawn beamed with pride.

*

Arthur had a great time on the holiday. Dawn's parents lived near the sea, and Arthur spent many sunny days on the beach playing with the other dogs he met there. At first he was scared of the sea, but eventually he plucked up the courage to have a modest paddle – with the water barely reaching the middle of his legs. But the young pup loved the sand and the rocks on the beach. He'd spend hours dragging big pebbles across the sand – as though he was building some sort of complicated city that only he knew how to design. He also loved a good romp with the other dogs on the beach, and it was while he was enjoying some rough-and-tumble with another German shepherd that Dawn noticed him limping. At first she thought he must have landed awkwardly, but as he continued to limp, and it got worse, Dawn felt a shadow pass over their holiday. If the limp was serious, Arthur would never become a guide dog. Arthur was holding up his right foreleg and made his way back from his fun and games to Dawn with pitiful puppy eyes. Dawn could see no sign of damage or injury, but there was obviously something wrong. Concerned, she called her Guide Dogs' supervisor back home in Scotland, who suggested that Dawn take Arthur to a vet in Devon. They X-rayed the pup, but couldn't find anything wrong.

Arthur continued to limp, so for the rest of the holiday Dawn kept him close to her. There would be no more fun afternoons frolicking with his friends on the beach. Arthur had to rest his leg. As a result his mood went from glum to utterly miserable. For the first time, he turned to Dawn for comfort. Perhaps it was the pain he was in – or perhaps just because they were spending so much time together, but Arthur seemed genuinely happy to be with Dawn. It was a turning-point for them both. Arthur had been the first pup Dawn hadn't really connected with straight away. At times during the first few months of his training she'd wondered whether he would make it. Sometimes he could be unfocused, and sometimes disobedient – as though he was constantly testing her to see what he could get away with. Now all of a sudden he was calmer and he was listening to her. He even seemed to be enjoying following her commands. Just as Dawn finally seemed to have won Arthur's trust he had become lame, jeopardising everything they'd been working for.

'Try not to fret . . .' Ian said soothingly. He was seeing Dawn and Arthur off in the car. They'd only just returned from Devon, and

Arthur was already booked in to see the Guide Dogs' own vet – a German shepherd specialist.

Dawn tried to smile, but it was hard. All of the other puppies she had looked after made it through to their advanced guide dog training. She couldn't bear it if Arthur failed. She'd grown fond of the independent little pup. While she still kept as much of an emotional distance from him as she could, when you spend time with a dog and pour so much energy and care into looking after them it is impossible not to love him them a little . . . and Arthur was easy to love. He was quirky, independent, slightly mischievous and bright as a button!

Thankfully, the diagnosis was quick: during a growth spurt, some of Arthur's growth plates hadn't developed at the same rate and, as a result, one leg had got out of sync with the others.

However, the vet was confident that Arthur would recover, with plenty of rest and care. Dawn felt a surge of relief for the dog. He would be OK; and he could still make it as a guide dog.

The vet was right. Within two months Arthur's limp gradually disappeared. By now Arthur had become a teenager in dog years. Just like all teenagers he was pushing the boundaries again; rebelling, and challenging Dawn as often as he could. As always, she was ready for him, but it was an exhausting time. Dawn had to reinforce everything she'd already taught him. She watched him constantly to make sure he was following her instructions. It wasn't really Arthur's fault. As a breed, German shepherds tend to be slower to mature than other dogs; much of his mischief was just down to pure high spirits. Dawn was aware that they were counting down the rest of the time that Arthur would be with them now. Every day was important because in just a few months' time Arthur would finish his puppy training and go on to advanced training, where he would have just weeks to prove himself. If he failed, then he was out forever!

As Christmas approached there was one particular issue that hung over them: cats! Whenever Arthur saw one he still barked – a lot! Even worse, he strained at his lead, desperate to give chase. Although cat-chasing was a common problem with German shepherds – after all it was their instinct to chase and herd. In order become a guide dog, the problem would have to be suppressed entirely. Otherwise he'd be a danger to his future owner, and the Guide Dogs team could never let that happen.

Logan Anderson, the Dog Supply Manager

at the Forfar training centre, where Arthur would soon be going, had a plan: cat therapy! During the Christmas holidays one of their most experienced guide dog instructors offered to have Arthur to stay with him at his home. As well as dogs of his own, he also had two strapping, no-nonsense cats. They were more than capable of giving a dog a bloody nose if he bothered them too much.

Arthur moved in temporarily with Iain McLachlan and his family, in a remote and beautiful glen. Arthur fitted in fast, loving the outdoor life. He also had some tough-love treatment courtesy of Iain's cats. Just as Logan had suspected, Arthur received a couple of bops on the nose. Iain's experience of dealing with this sort of problem, combined with the confident cats, seemed to quash Arthur's cat phobia for the moment, but it still wasn't completely fixed.

Logan hoped that as Arthur matured they'd be able to sort it out. They would tackle it again as soon as he moved on to his advanced training.

Then, finally, that day came. It was a beautiful morning, the sun shone and there was a taste of spring in the air. It was the day that Arthur had to leave Dawn. Arthur, along with nineteen other dogs, would move on to advanced training at the Forfar training centre. It would be an intense time for the dogs. The instructors would begin by bonding with them and reinforcing the skills they'd already learned in puppy training: obedience, self-control, how to cope on buses and trains, around crowds and with loud noises. They would also be taught new skills: how to stop and sit when they reached a kerb, how to avoid obstacles, navigate stairs, and how to work wearing a harness. They would have just eighteen weeks to prove themselves. At any point they could fail – and many did. Only the best would be allowed to continue. If they made it through, they would be matched with an owner and receive their final training specially tailored around the lifestyle of that person.

For Arthur it was a huge mountain to climb. Only half of all the German shepherds went on to qualify as guide dogs. Would he do it? Dawn still wasn't certain. She was sure he *could* do it, but would he?

The car was waiting. Dawn bent down to give Arthur a final cuddle. She swallowed back the tears that always came at this point and softly whispered 'Good bye and good luck' in his ear. She told him she loved him and then waved him off. In many respects Arthur's journey was just beginning. He had so much still to learn. Dawn knew he had it in him to be a brilliant guide dog and she really hoped he would make it. That little pup with the giant bat-like ears had already come such a long way. With lots of hard work, he'd make it. And if he didn't? Well, Dawn had already decided. She would offer him a home and have him back with her again. If he couldn't be a guide dog, then he could spend the rest of his days as her dog.

Cara

It was the morning of the wedding. Everyone was rushing to get ready. Andrea was in a hurry too – in just over an hour her big sister, Dawn, would be marrying her fiancé, Neil, and there was still so much to do. It wasn't just herself she had to organize, she had Cara to get ready too.

Cara was Andrea's guide dog, but today she also had the important role of the official ring-bearer. She would walk behind the bride, carrying the wedding rings inside a little pink bag tied to her collar. She had to look her best!

Andrea started with Cara's silky black coat. Always shiny, it almost sparkled after a good brush. Then there were her teeth to be cleaned (good breath was essential for a wedding!). Finally, there was her new collar to put on, which was pink and dotted with sparkling diamanté. The little bag for the wedding rings was attached underneath, next to the badge which displayed her name in big, bold letters. At last she was ready. Then it was Andrea's turn. She ran her hand over her pretty teal-blue bridesmaid's dress that was hanging on her wardrobe door. It was going to be a good day.

In fact it was the perfect day for a wedding: bright sunshine, birds singing and the soft smell of flowers drifting gently around the front of the church as Dawn and her bridesmaids arrived. As Dawn stepped out of the wedding car Andrea could hear the organ playing inside the church. A group of wedding watchers had gathered by the wall and called 'Good luck!' to Dawn while the photographer clicked away. There was just time to smooth Dawn's dress and make some final adjustments before Dawn's mum took her arm, ready to walk her daughter down the aisle and give her away. Andrea followed close behind, with Cara beside her. 'Good girl,' Andrea whispered. She stroked the dog's silky black head and then reached down to check her collar, just to be sure that the little pink bag was still there.

Then the organ music suddenly changed tempo and the wedding march began. 'This is it,' Andrea whispered to Cara, 'Time to go . . .' Together they set off through the big church doors. Andrea smiled as she felt the familiar warmth of Cara by her side. It was hard to believe that just three years ago she had had to battle to have her guide dog; and now here she was, playing a big part in her sister's wedding.

All heads in the church turned to see Dawn

and her mum as they walked down the aisle. Andrea and Cara followed behind along with the other bridesmaids. Waiting at the altar was Dawn's fiancé, Neil, and his best man. As Andrea reached them, she untied the little bag and handed it over, and the wedding service began . . .

Andrea had been fourteen years old when the idea of a guide dog had first been suggested. Like most teenagers, the older she got, the more freedom and independence she wanted. But unlike her friends, she had to rely on other people to take her everywhere.

'I mean – as much as I love him – who wants to be walked to school by their brother every day!' she told Janice, her mobility instructor.

It was Janice who first thought of a guide dog. Most guide dog owners were older, but

Janice had heard about a new scheme specifically aimed at teenagers. It was a pilot project to see if young people could benefit from having guide dogs too. The Guide Dog Association also wanted to see if guide dogs could cope in school. Andrea loved the idea immediately. She was a highly intelligent girl; bright, motivated and determined. She was the youngest of five, and had a twin brother. Despite being born virtually blind, she had never let her sight problems stop her from joining in with the other kids. She didn't go to a special school. She went to the same one as her brothers and sister. She did her schoolwork by using a computer and touch typing — remembering where the individual keys on the keyboard were, rather than seeing them — and also by using a screen reader, a device which reads aloud textbooks and work sheets. She played the same games as the other kids.

She did the same lessons. She worked hard and got good marks. If anyone could make having a guide dog work for a teenager, Andrea could! But getting everyone else to agree turned out to be a bigger problem than either Andrea or Janice had expected.

Andrea's family were behind her all the way, but some of her teachers were worried. How would a guide dog fit in at school? Where would it eat? What if it needed to go to the toilet? What if other children's parents didn't like it?

It wasn't just the teachers who were concerned. Sensory Support Services, the council department that helped Andrea at school by providing the equipment and support she needed, were worried too. They thought she was too young for a guide dog and that the dog wouldn't be able to cope with the noise and distractions at school.

However, Andrea was determined. 'After all,' she explained to her mum, 'they don't need to rely on a friend to walk them to class, or take them to the dinner hall, or to the bathroom door!'

Andrea's mum agreed. She was also determined that Andrea should have the chance to do everything other kids did. She'd always felt that way, ever since she'd first realized Andrea had a problem with her sight. When she was a small baby the doctors thought Andrea was totally blind, but her mum knew differently. She'd noticed that Andrea *did* actually reach out for things — but only if they were held directly in front of her. Eventually she was diagnosed with a condition called optic atrophy — like severe tunnel vision. Andrea had a tiny pinprick of vision, straight ahead, but she could see nothing surrounding it or to the sides. Being part of a big lively family,

Andrea never let her lack of sight stop her . . . or slow her down. She frequently had accidents, banging into pillar boxes, or crashing into walls and parked cars. When she was small, she just picked herself up, dusted herself down (checking to make sure she hadn't broken any bones), then carried on playing! As she got older, she became more self-conscious about the bumps and bruises and black eyes. She started to slow down. She lost some of her confidence, and became embarrassed when she had an accident. She tried using a long cane, but that didn't help much. At the same time, her need for independence was growing. She desperately wanted to be like her friends and be able to go shopping by herself, or pop round to see her mates. Now, suddenly, with the help of a guide dog, it looked like that dream might become a reality. First, she would need her school's support.

Thankfully, she got it. Despite the concerns of some members of staff, Andrea's head teacher William Wolger, was immediately on her side. He was an inspirational man who'd always been supportive and encouraging of Andrea. If she thought she could manage a guide dog, he would back her all the way. He signed her consent form immediately, promising to do everything he could to help. Then he sent out a letter to all the other parents, telling them that one of the pupils would be returning at the start of the next term with a guide dog. As far as he was concerned, there was never any question about it – it was happening, and that was that!

The seventh of August 2006 was a day Andrea would never forget; it was the day she met Cara. As Andrea and her mum stepped out of the cars at the Guide Dogs training centre in Leamington

Cara

Spa she felt the warm sun on her face. Summer was slipping gently into autumn, and there was freshness in the air. Andrea had butterflies in her tummy, but she wasn't frightened – the fluttering feeling was due to excitement. She felt like she was on the cusp of change. Somehow, she knew today was the first day of the rest of her life; a new life of independence and freedom. There would be hard work, of course, but Andrea was ready for it.

Her mum squeezed her hand. Then Andrea opened the front door and together they went inside.

Cara had been carefully chosen for Andrea. Matching a guide dog with its owner is complicated – everything has to be considered; the owner's height, build, the length of their stride and the pace they walk at. Their lifestyle is important too. If the owner spends a lot of time travelling or walking or doing activities, then they would need a dog with the strength and stamina to keep up. If there were children in the house, the dog would need to fit in with them. If they were used to travelling on buses or trains, the dog would have to be able to cope. Most importantly, there was the question of temperament. The dog and owner would need to be suited to each other as friends; best friends, even – after all, they could be working and living together for the next seven or eight years. There had to be a bond between the dog and its owner.

For Andrea and Cara that bond was immediate.

'There's just something about her,' Andrea said to her mum as she wrapped her arms around the beautiful black Labrador's neck. 'I just feel a connection with her.'

Andrea's mum could see it too. Although Andrea didn't have a pet dog of her own, she'd grown up spending time with her grandparents' dogs. Labradors were a breed the family knew and loved.

'Your grandad's going to love her,' Mum smiled.

And he did! But before Andrea could take Cara home she had to stay at the training centre for a few days and learn how to work with her.

It was hard; much harder than Andrea had imagined. The dog had already been trained. Now Andrea had to be trained too — so that she was able to give the right commands, use the right gestures, say the right thing and take control. It wasn't like the playing she'd done with her grandparents' dogs. This was work; teamwork. If she got it wrong, Cara would get it wrong too.

One of hardest parts of the training was learning to trust Cara. When she picked up the dog's harness Andrea had to trust that Cara wouldn't let anything happen to her. It was a leap of faith.

At first Andrea moved slowly and cautiously, but Cara wanted to go faster. Andrea could feel her tugging on the harness – it was a strange sensation. As Cara escorted Andrea around the training course – avoiding obstacles, stopping at kerbstones and weaving in and out of cones, it was hard for Andrea to keep up at first. She kept expecting to bump into things and felt nervous as a result.

Andrea's mum, who was watching from the side, could see that Andrea was finding it difficult. There seemed to be a mini power-struggle going on – with Cara wanting to lead, and Andrea holding back, nervous and unsure.

Gradually, with each new turn around the course, Andrea's mum saw her daughter relax. Her shoulders softened. Her back straightened. Andrea began to walk faster, keeping pace with Cara. The dog sensed it too. The more Andrea seemed to enjoy working with her, the happier and more confident Cara became. This was a big change for the dog too. She had been a cautious puppy. There had even been moments during her puppy training when the centre's staff had thought she would fail. She was a worrier; she'd even suffered from hair loss, brought on by stress during her puppyhood. Yet here she was, finally in harness with her new owner and growing more confident by the minute, with Andrea growing in confidence beside her. They seemed to take confidence from one another. Andrea was right. There *was* a connection!

They worked together at the training

centre for five days. Then the training moved to Andrea's home, so that Cara could become familiar with the regular routes they would use. Andrea also needed to get used to caring for the dog; another essential skill a guide dog owner has to learn. There were routines to build: feeding, toileting and exercise.

Then, suddenly, the training stopped and real life kicked in. It was the first day of the new school term and Andrea was planning to walk to school alone for the first time.

'Are you sure you don't want to come with me?' Andrew, her twin, asked. For the past ten years he'd cheerfully escorted his sister everywhere, and now she suddenly didn't need him.

'I'll be fine,' Andrea smiled. 'We'll be fine!' She crossed her fingers and took a deep breath. She was nervous but trying not to show it. Then she reached down and stroked Cara's head. Since the first day of training they'd been inseparable. Cara slept in Andrea's room; she dozed by her feet when she was on the computer. Even when they went to the park and Cara was off duty and allowed some free play she still kept close to Andrea's side.

Andrew grinned. 'OK, see you there, then!' Suddenly Andrea and Cara were on their own! As soon as Andrea put on Cara's harness, the dog immediately stood taller. It was as though she'd put on her uniform and was now on duty. They'd practised the route to school during a training session, but now it was for real.

It was a slightly nervous first walk, but they did it. 'Good girl, Cara,' Andrea whispered, beaming with pride as they finally approached the school gates.

They were surrounded by chattering

teenagers and Andrea wondered whether the noise might scare Cara, but her dog didn't falter a bit. She did her job perfectly. Andrea felt a surge of excitement as she went through the school doors alone for the first time. After fifteen years of needing help from other people, at last Andrea felt independent.

Of course the kids at school loved Cara. They weren't supposed to make a fuss of her when she was on duty, but at breaktimes, when Cara was resting, there was always a queue to give her a cuddle. Cara enjoyed the attention, but she never let it distract her. During lessons Cara settled underneath Andrea's desk, waiting patiently until she was needed again. At lunchtime, she showed remarkable self-control in the dinner hall, which was quite amazing for a Labrador, as they tend to be ruled by their stomachs! When she needed a toilet break Cara did her business quickly and was back on duty in moments. This last issue had worried some of Andrea's teachers, but it wasn't a problem at all. Guide Dogs had installed a small concrete pen for her, well away from the main school building, and this was where she would go. It was something she'd been taught to do as a puppy – to go to the toilet at regular times of the day and in a certain place. So that by the time she was in harness, there were never any accidents. No fuss, no mess, and back to work very quickly.

'We did it!' The first day was over, and Andrea and Cara were walking home. Andrea couldn't stop grinning. She felt a bubble of excitement in her stomach. They'd conquered school on their first day together. Now there would be no stopping them. They could go anywhere; do anything. And they did!

Over the next few weeks there were more new experiences, including their first bus trip (Andrea had fully expected to end up completely lost, but it had turned out to be much easier than she'd expected) and Andrea's first solo shopping trip. That was harder – getting to the city centre was fine, but once she was there she wasn't sure where the individual shops were. After a few tries, she learned her way around, and so did Cara.

Very soon, Andrea's world expanded. There were visits to the cinema, the theatre, bowling, or just hanging out with her mates at their houses. Having Cara changed Andrea's life overnight. As a result she was growing in confidence. Her grades, which had always been good, were even better now. Andrea was seriously considering going to university – something she hadn't thought she could do before she had Cara. Suddenly anything seemed possible.

Cara

*

Then there was the wedding . . .

Cara had fitted in with the family right from the start. She adored Andrea, and was her constant companion. She also had a soft spot for Andrea's twin Andrew, and their big sister Dawn. Andrea's grandad was another favourite. A dog-lover himself, he looked forward to Cara's weekend visit, when they would play together in the fields next to his house. As one of the family, Dawn was keen that Cara should be part of her wedding too and the role of ring-bearer seemed ideal. As always, Cara did her job perfectly. She wasn't frightened by the church or the noise – the organ music, the bells or the crowds of well-wishing, confetti-throwing guests, who gathered around her afterwards to stroke and make a fuss of her. She thoroughly enjoyed the attention – even joining in the family photos!

*

Much later, after the final wedding guests had gone home, Andrea lay in her bed remembering the day. It had been brilliant; and so had Cara. Andrea reached out her hand to gently stroke Cara's head. They had already achieved so much. In a few weeks' time, they would start their biggest adventure of all. University! Andrea had done it. She'd passed her exams and got the grades she needed to start a degree at the University of Warwick. It would mean a two-hour round trip on the bus each day, and hard work, and lots of new challenges. With Cara's help, Andrea knew she could cope. After that? She wasn't sure . . . teaching maybe, social work, perhaps. Whatever she chose, she felt confident she could do it. Andrea was an amazing person in many ways. As one of the youngest people ever to own a guide dog she was a pioneer –

a trailblazer for other teenagers who would follow her example. She was brave and determined. She had the positive attitude to achieve whatever she wanted in life and Cara had given her the independence and confidence to do just that. 'Thanks, girl . . .' she whispered. 'Goodnight . . .' She blew a small kiss to Cara, who was now fast asleep by her bed. Whatever Andrea chose, she knew she would not be alone. Cara, as her loyal companion, would be with her, every step of the way.

Gus

The city centre was busy now. It was lunchtime, and the pavements were filling up with hungry office workers, schoolchildren and shoppers. Jemma Brown was on her way to her university. It was a route she and her guide dog, Gus, followed most days – a straight path through the centre of Southampton. It was a sunny day and Jemma could feel the warmth of the sun on her face. She was thinking about that evening, when she was planning a trip home to see her parents – a visit she knew Gus would love.

And that's when it happened. Just as Jemma and Gus passed one of the busy cafes, another dog suddenly appeared from nowhere. Enormous, growling, it charged at them. Jemma tried to shield Gus – but her gentle black retriever cross was no match for this beast. But it was impossible. The dog leaped at Gus, sinking its teeth into the guide dog's neck. Jemma shouted and tried to fend off the dog, but she couldn't see what was happening; virtually blind, the small amount of vision Jemma still had disappeared altogether on sunny days like this. 'Let go!' she yelled, trying to shove the animal off. She couldn't see it, but she could hear the snarling, and feel the weight of it on Gus's harness. She could also hear Gus's cries; shrill – almost like screams – sounds chilled her. 'Get off him!' she yelled again, more desperate now. The animal just tightened its grip on Gus's throat. Then Jemma felt the harness strain as Gus lurched sideways. Jemma looked around for help, and then, finally, the animal's owners stepped in.

'Get your dog off!' shouted Jemma. The two men were unfriendly and intimidating; they started swearing at their dog. Then one tried to drag it off, but it ignored them, snarling and biting Gus even harder. Then one of the men started hitting his dog. A stray punch hit Gus, flooring the guide dog completely. He lay still then, his eyes closed, his breathing heavy . . .

'Gus?' Jemma tried to reach out to him, but the other dog was still attacking him. Then suddenly it stopped. The dog took off down the street, barking fiercely. The men followed, pushing past Jemma and disappearing after their ferocious animal.

For a moment Jemma just froze. And then she felt a gentle hand on her arm: 'Are you all right?' It was a man who'd been in the cafe nearby. 'I saw what happened,' he said. 'It was a giant boxer – an enormous thing – big and white . . .

but it's gone now . . . you're safe . . .'

Jemma couldn't speak. Her whole body was shaking. She crouched down and reached out to Gus. She felt blood. 'Gus?' she whispered, her voice breaking. There was no response. 'GUS? Come on, boy, come on now . . .' Still nothing.

'He's in a bad way . . .' the man said gently.

Jemma stroked her dog's head. 'Come on now,' she said softly. 'Hang in there, boy, I need you.'

It was true. Although they'd only been together just over a year, Jemma couldn't imagine life without Gus. The bond between them was strong. Right from the moment she'd met him she'd felt an instant connection with the dog, and it seemed like he'd felt it too. It was as though he'd been waiting for Jemma all his life, and now he'd found her he wasn't going to let her go. The day they'd met, Gus had laid himself down at her feet as she filled in the forms, and the pair had been best friends ever since.

Jemma had been ninteen years old at the time, and just about to go off to university. She'd wanted to get her dog before she started so they could settle in to their new life together. It had worked out well. Jemma's world opened up as a result of having Gus. He gave her the confidence to leave home, move into student accommodation and become more independent. She made friends. She settled into student life well. Best of all, in Gus, she found a soulmate – which was why it was so hard to sit next to him now – unconscious and covered in blood.

'I've called the police. They'll be here soon.' Another man from the cafe had joined the small crowd comforting Jemma.

'Thank you,' she whispered. 'Thank you all . . .' She cradled Gus's head in her lap. Her heart was racing. Her hands shaking, she wiped the tears off her cheeks. She wasn't sure what to do next – without Gus, she couldn't get home. Then, suddenly, another thought occurred to her . . . Just moments before the attack she'd met a friend from the Guide Dogs training centre. The lady had been out walking some new pups, guide dogs in training. I must warn them, she thought to herself. What if that dog gets them too . . .

Jemma searched for her mobile phone. Her hands still shaking, she dialled the Guide Dogs office and told them about the attack. Just as she finished speaking the police arrived.

Still shaking, Jemma explained in detail what had happened. Others did too: the cafe's customers and passers-by who had witnessed the attack gave detailed statements to the police. But the dog and its owners had long since gone.

Meanwhile, Gus had come round. Bravely, he struggled back to his feet, taking up his usual position, close by Jemma's side. But he was in a bad way. His breathing was heavy, and he was shaking slightly. The wounds on his neck looked painful and were still bleeding.

The team manager from the Guide Dogs training centre arrived just after the police. He drove them to the vet's, where they cleaned up Gus's wounds and checked him over to make sure nothing was broken. The future effect of the head injury – where the man had punched him – was hard to predict. Concussion could have serious consequences. 'Just keep a close eye on him,' the vet told Jemma.

A few hours later, Jemma finally made it into the university and collected the work she needed. Then she and Gus made their way back through the city centre, heading for the bus station. It was the end of the day now. Shops were closing. The traffic was getting heavier as people headed home for the night.

As they retraced their steps along the street where the attack had happened, Jemma wondered whether Gus would cope. He had to. If Gus refused to walk that route, she wouldn't be able to go to university any more. He had to do it . . . She held her breath as they reached and then passed the exact place where it had happened. Gus seemed nervous, anxious even . . . but he did it. They did it; together.

Jemma was weary now. More than anything she wanted to go home – not to her student digs, but to her real home, where her mum and dad were waiting, a place where she would be safe, and Gus would be too. Only then would she be able to rest and recover from the shock of the attack.

'Are you sure he'll be OK?'

It was three days later, and Jemma was still at home, but now she was packing. In just a few hours' time she was due to fly to Switzerland – escorting thirty Girl Guides on a visit there. As well as doing a degree, Jemma was a Girl Guide leader – and she frequently led groups of girls on visits and activities. She had agreed to help out on the trip months ago – her parents were going to take care of Gus – but now, after the attack, she wasn't sure if she could leave him.

'I don't want to go.' Jemma hugged Gus close. He wagged his tail in reply. In the three days since the attack he'd recovered a bit – but he was still much quieter than normal.

'He'll be fine, I'll take care of him.' Jemma's

mum stroked the dog's silky black head. 'Besides, he's got his two best friends here.'

It was true. Jemma's mum was registered blind too – and she not only had her current guide dog, Tara, living there – she also had her previous dog, Ian, who was now retired. Both dogs adored Gus. The three of them liked nothing better than to play in the garden. That was one of the reasons why Gus loved going to visit Jemma's parents so much – he got to see his friends.

Jemma smiled at her mum. Her own confidence had been badly knocked by the attack too: she had felt vulnerable and unsafe. This trip to Switzerland would be good for her – leading a group of youngsters, all of them looking to her for support and encouragement, would give her back some of the confidence that she'd lost. . . .

'I'll miss you, Gus,' she said, burying her face

into his soft fur. He wagged his tail some more, then rested his head on her shoulder. It was as though he understood exactly how she felt.

Jemma was gone ten days. It was a busy trip – but she still found time to call home regularly: 'How's Gus?' she would ask her mum.

'Fine, missing you,' her mum said. Her mum didn't tell Jemma was that Gus was ill. The day after she left for her trip he'd been quite sick. He was off his food, listless and weary. Jemma's parents had taken him to the emergency vet. His neck wounds were infected and the effects of the concussion were starting to show. For one long night, Jemma's mum sat up with him – Gus had been very ill. For a while, Jemma's parents thought they might lose him altogether . . . but by the following morning he'd rallied slightly. 'I can't tell her,' Jemma's mum had said to her dad, when the phone rang the following day. 'She'd be worried sick.' Her dad agreed it was better not to tell Jemma while she was away. So, by the time she returned home from the trip, Gus was much better. But when Jemma heard what her dog had been through, her distress and concern for Gus turned to anger; anger at the people who had allowed their dog to attack him. She was also worried it might happen to others, not just other dogs, but possibly children too.

She wrote to her local council, demanding that they take action against irresponsible dog owners. 'I mean, why shouldn't all dogs have to be on a lead in the city centre?' she said to her mum. 'It would be so much safer for everyone. Imagine if that dog had attacked a child . . . ?'

Other people agreed. Jemma was interviewed in the local newspaper and was on national television talking about the problem. She discovered it wasn't just her and Gus who'd suffered such attacks. It was a growing problem across the country – as many as three guide dogs a month were being attacked by other dogs. They were easy targets; trained to be obedient, gentle and steady, guide dogs were unlikely to fight back. While the physical injuries guide dogs received in these attacks were often relatively minor, the psychological effect on the dogs was huge. Some guide dogs were unable to work again. Others – like Gus – battled on, to support their beloved owners, but were left nervous and anxious around other dogs, as Jemma discovered when she went back to university.

They were walking in the city centre again when it happened. Another dog was approaching them. Gus was immediately alert and uncomfortable. He barked as the other dog approached. This was unusual behaviour for

Gus – guide dogs are trained not to bark at other dogs when they are working. But the incident had changed Gus and he was scared and tense. Whenever another dog approached him, he presumed it might attack.

Unfortunately, Gus was right. Over the next eighteen months, two more dogs attacked him. In one attack, Jemma and her friends were walking back from church – across a park – when a Rottweiler charged them, heading straight for Gus. Thankfully, a friend of Jemma's managed to get in between the two dogs and bravely grabbed the Rottweiler's collar and dragged him off. Another time, a bad-tempered Jack Russell terrier ran across a road to attack Gus – only stopping when his owner eventually came and took him away. Despite the attacks, Gus was steadfast and loyal, ready to sacrifice himself to stay by Jemma's side. It was this bravery that eventually won Gus a top award.

Every year Guide Dogs rewards dogs who make a real difference to their owner's life, and in 2010, Gus was named Exceptional Work Guide Dog of the Year. Jemma was understandably proud. Despite everything Gus had been through he was still an unbelievable guide dog.

Jemma leads a busy life. She devotes much of her time to helping others – as well as being a student and a Girl Guide leader, she helps out in her local church. She also plays cricket for Hampshire Country Cricket Club – and trains other youngsters to play too. Because of her cricket and her voluntary work, she travels a lot, which means Gus frequently has to escort Jemma in unfamiliar towns and cities, and on trains and even the London Underground – which, for some reason, he loves! It was this adaptability and dependability that won him the award. Nothing phases Gus. He is always ready to go anywhere with Jemma: to cricket matches, camping trips, the cinema, Girl Guide meetings — or even to a pop concert. Every Sunday, he joins her at church — where the sound of the congregation's full-on rock band doesn't bother him. He just snoozes peacefully in one of the pews. Jemma had known from the start that Gus was special. Now, with his award, everyone else knows it too. Her steadfast best friend is a true brave heart — and now he has the award to prove it!

Jamie

It was the hottest weekend of the year; thirty degrees in the shade. Sidney and his guide dog, Jamie, had been walking for hours. 'Come on boy, you can do it . . . just one more mile.' Sidney stroked the dog's hot head and then wiped his own brow. He tried not to think of his aching feet and weary legs. They'd been trekking all day – and now, with just a mile or so to go, Sidney suddenly felt exhaustion sweep over him. At his feet, Jamie was panting as though he'd spent all his energy, and all he had left was sheer determination to do a good job for his owner.

'Good lad, have some more water.' Sidney crouched down and reached into his rucksack to pull out a bottle. He filled a small dish and gave it to Jamie, then he opened another bottle for himself. Sidney knew that if they stayed sitting there for much longer, they'd never get up again. With a sigh he put the empty bowl and bottles back in his rucksack and hauled himself up.

'Come on then, let's go.' Instantly, Jamie was on his feet and ready. He would do anything for Sidney, even spend three days trekking through dense forest, scrambling up hillsides and sliding down muddy banks! 'It'll be worth it when we finish!' said Sidney, grinning, picking up the dog's harness. As if in reply, Jamie wagged his tail and, wearily, the pair trudged off again.

It had all seemed like such a good idea when they'd signed up for it. At eighteen years old Sidney had already completed his bronze Duke of Edinburgh's Award, a national scheme for young people aged between fourteen and twenty-four years old, consisting of a series of personal challenges and activities. It hadn't been easy. To get the award, Sidney had had to learn lots of new skills, such as playing the guitar and drums, and to complete physical challenges, including camping overnight in the forest and learning to play blind football. When the opportunity to go for his Silver Award had come up, Sidney couldn't resist the challenge. It would be even tougher than the Bronze Award had been, but Sidney wasn't afraid of much. The prospect of roughing it in a forest for three days didn't worry him. There would be fire-making, camp-building, cooking and the small matter of a three-day-30-mile hike, using just a map and compass to navigate. It would be tough enough for a person with perfect sight to complete, but for Sidney, who had only limited vision, it would be a huge challenge. Sidney was sure he could do it, though. After all, he had his secret weapon: Jamie!

Sidney had been one of the youngest people in the country to have a guide dog. He started his training just a couple of months after his fifteenth birthday.

Both Sidney's parents had sight loss, and both had their own guide dogs, so Sidney had grown up around guide dogs and knew the difference they made to a blind person's life, and he was now ready for a dog of his own.

Sidney had inherited an eye condition called glaucoma. This meant he was registered blind although he had a very small amount of sight – he could make out some shapes and outlines and tell the difference between light and dark.

His sight loss made it difficult to move around independently, but just like all teenagers, that's exactly what Sidney wanted — to have the freedom to choose where to go and when, so he jumped at the opportunity to join a new pilot scheme offering teenagers their own guide dogs.

He could still remember the first day he'd met Jamie. As soon as the dog saw him, he'd trotted over and laid his head on Sidney's lap. The gentle golden retriever/Labrador cross quickly became Sidney's best friend. He was a placid dog, kind-hearted and good fun. Everyone loved him. He fitted in straight away at Sidney's school. He escorted Sidney to his lessons and gave him the confidence and independence to focus on his studies and get the grades he needed to go on to college to study business and computing. It wasn't just school Jamie helped with. Overnight, he'd changed Sidney's life by enabling him to take on all sorts of new challenges, like the Duke of Edinburgh's Award . . .

'Come on, Jamie . . . We can do this . . . really we can!' There wasn't much further to go now – but they were both flagging. Jamie had slowed right down and Sidney wasn't much faster. There were two small teams participating in the award, seven teenagers in total, and all of them had sight loss, but Sidney was the only one with a guide dog. That meant he not only had to carry his own gear on his back, his tent, clothes and provisions, but Jamie's dog food, bedding, water and bowl too. Despite the heat and his aching bones (they'd already hiked twenty miles by this stage), Sidney was loving the experience. He was an outdoors lad at heart.

Sidney's dad had introduced him to camping

as a young boy and had taught him how to put up a tent. Which was just as well, because for this challenge he not only had to put up his tent, but then take it down each morning and carry it to the next location before putting it up again! Sidney's dad had also taught him how to cook on a small camping stove, which was another very useful skill. Sidney was learning lots of new things as well. The previous evening a huge pile of wood was needed to keep the camp fire burning so Sidney had received a lesson in log-chopping! Sidney's arms ached afterwards – in fact, after all the hiking, everything ached; even muscles he hadn't come across before now throbbed with pain – and they still had a mile or so to go. Sidney gritted his teeth. 'Come on, Jamie,' he puffed, '. . . nearly there.' The dog surged on. Somehow, he seemed to realize how close they were now and the urge to get there spurred him on. Sidney could feel him pulling harder on the harness, and he smiled.

This wasn't the first adventure the pair had been on. Three years ago Sidney and Jamie had got the chance to go to Centre Court at Wimbledon to toss the coin in the men's tennis singles final!

As a life-long tennis fan Sidney couldn't believe his luck when he had got the phone call. Each year Wimbledon chose a charity to support and that year it was Guide Dogs. As one of the youngest guide dog owners in the country Sidney was an inspiration for other teenagers who would follow in his footsteps. He had been asked to represent the charity and toss the coin to decide who served first in the final between Roger Federer and Rafael Nadal. Sidney was understandably nervous about the job – what if he dropped the coin in front of the entire Centre Court crowd? Not to mention the millions watching at home on television! But Jamie wasn't worried in the slightest. When the time came he confidently led Sidney on to court as if they were just out for a Sunday stroll, and Sidney did his job perfectly too. Federer won the toss and went on to win Wimbledon as well.

Sidney remembered that day now as he trudged down the track with Jamie. It had been hot at Wimbledon, but nothing like this weekend. The sweat poured down his back and he longed to take off his boots, have a cold drink and rest.

The trail they were following was rough underfoot. It would have been tough going for a sighted person, let alone someone who was visually impaired, like Sidney. There were hazards everywhere: fallen branches, thick tree roots, rotting logs and boulders strewn along the narrow paths. There were steep hillsides and muddy gullies too. Jamie was doing an amazing job at keeping them both safe. He was concentrating hard – just as Sidney was. Indeed, Sidney had wondered how Jamie would cope in a forest with so many potential distractions for a dog; small furry animals scurrying around, interesting scents and lots of sticks he'd love to chew, but Jamie never wavered. As soon as he was in a harness he was on duty.

After a while Sidney stopped for a moment to check his map and compass. They were specially adapted for people with sight loss: tactile and written in Braille. The group also had a voice recorder with them, which gave them brief instructions on the route to take. 'I think we bend left now,' Sidney said as another member of their group caught up with them. He agreed. Sidney had an instinct for navigation. There was also something very dependable about him. He had a quiet confidence which inspired trust from others. He never panicked. He was always calm.

The small group rested for a moment. They drank water, caught their breath, and then, with Sidney and Jamie at the front once more, they headed off for what they hoped would be their final stretch. The sun had peaked now, and it was cooler in the shade. The trees were beginning to thin out and they were approaching the clearing . . . 'This is it, Jamie, we're almost there, I'm sure of it . . .' The dog picked up the pace in response, carefully weaving around several large rocks that were just ahead of them on the path. Finally, when all their energy was almost exhausted, they were there. They had reached the second campsite.

★

They rested, but not for long. There was a camp to build.

'It's all right for you,' grinned Sidney, ruffling Jamie's ears playfully. 'You get to rest your paws, while I have to put up the tent and make your tea!'

Jamie thumped his tail up and down in response, but made no attempt to get up. It was just too nice resting, waiting for his dinner to be served.

There were loads of jobs to do: logs to chop, a fire to build and dinner to cook. The team worked together to cook a meal. It was pasta tonight: a basic dish, but to the hungry campers it tasted like food from a five-star restaurant. After they'd tidied up there were a few songs around the campfire, stories and chat, and then gradually, one by one, everyone headed for their tent and to bed. The heat of the day had long since gone, replaced by the chill of the early summer night. Sidney snuggled deeper into his sleeping bag and was glad to have the warmth of Jamie by his side. He stretched out on the hard ground and sighed as each muscle in turn began to relax – and then throb! He grinned and said to his dog, 'And we've got to do it all again tomorrow . . .' Next to him, Jamie stirred and groaned slightly, as though he understood exactly what Sidney was saying and was trying hard not to think about it. Moments later they were both asleep, and the camp was silent.

The peace didn't last long. Sidney woke suddenly to find Jamie standing up, staring at the tent door, alert, listening intently. 'What is it, lad?' Sidney patted the dog reassuringly. Jamie didn't move. His ears were up, his tail down . . . and then Sidney heard it . . . a deep growling sort of a noise in the distance – not like a dog. In fact, not like anything Sidney had ever heard before. It was far away and difficult to make out, but as Sidney sat and listened it grew slightly louder. There was a rustling and snorting sound too, and he could hear the sound of branches breaking, as though the beast was foraging for something. Jamie didn't like it. His body was tense. His eyes fixed on the tent door.

'All right, Jamie, it's all right . . .' Sidney stroked his head . . . 'It's probably just a fox . . . or maybe a badger . . .'

But Jamie didn't move. Sidney listened again. The noise was closer now and getting louder. For a moment Sidney thought the creature – whatever it might be – was heading for their camp . . . He climbed out of his sleeping bag and went to open the tent flap. The noise suddenly stopped. Sidney froze and listened. This time when he heard the sound again it was much further away. The creature was moving away from their camp. Jamie's body softened as he started to relax. He lay down and was calm again. Sidney sat listening for another five minutes or so, but the noise had vanished entirely now. He wriggled wearily back into his bag and was just drifting off to sleep, when suddenly he realized exactly what the creature must have been – a wild boar! The Forest of Dean, where they were camping, was famous for them. There were thought to be more than a hundred wild boars living in the forest. Nobody was certain where they had come from – some thought they'd been deliberately released there, others said they'd escaped from farms. Although shy, they could be aggressive and troublesome. There were reports of them attacking dogs and horses in the forest. Sidney was relieved the creature had chosen to give their camp a wide berth, but he was also excited to have heard it. It just added to the adventure.

The morning hit them like a wall. Sidney groaned and buried his head inside his sleeping bag. He ached all over. Every muscle seemed to shout in protest whenever he moved. The thought of getting up, putting his boots back on and walking another ten miles or so filled him with dread. He tried to go back to sleep, but Jamie wasn't having any of it. He was up and ready, raring to go again. He stood over Sidney, butting him playfully through the sleeping bag, urging him to get up and get his breakfast! 'All right, all right, Jamie, you win!' said Sidney wearily.

After a tasty fry-up — cooked by himself — Sidney felt much better. A gentle morning sunlight, the kind that fills you with hope and energy, shone over them, which was a welcome change from the exhausting intensity of the sun the previous day. As Sidney packed up his tent and belongings for the final time he felt almost sad that it would soon be over. Although not too sad – the blisters throbbing inside his walking boots saw to that! In just a few hours' time they would finish the trek and be on the minibus heading back home again. It had been an adventure neither of them would forget!

As they set off down the trail together once again, Sidney felt a deep sense of peace and contentment. This was what life was all about. Setting yourself a challenge, meeting it, exceeding it and succeeding against the odds. Sidney had been doing that all his life, and now with the help of Jamie, he was able to achieve even more.

94

Jamie

*

Much later, exhausted and aching, Sidney and Jamie finally reached the end of their trek. Sidney had not only completed his silver Duke of Edinburgh Award, he'd also made it into the record books. He and Jamie were the first visually impaired owner and guide dog to achieve the award. It had been a huge challenge, and Sidney, with Jamie's help, had been more than a match for it. Sidney was an inspiration. He was brave, he was positive and he'd never let his sight loss stop him from achieving his goals. The more he achieved, the higher he aimed. As he untied his walking boots he was already planning their next adventure: the Duke of Edinburgh's Gold Award! Jamie though, was blissfully unaware. He was snoring softly and curled up in his favourite place, close to Sidney's feet: ever ready and on hand as soon as Sidney needed him.

Josie

Emma peered out into the gloom of the garden and sighed. 'It's *still* raining,' she said. 'The middle of the summer holidays, and it's pouring down!'

'Mmm . . . .' Her mum, Lynne, didn't look up. She was sitting on the living-room floor close to Josie, the family dog, patting her gently on the top of her head.

'The garden is starting to look like a duck pond!' grumbled Emma. 'Mmm . . .' Her mum still didn't look up.

'If it doesn't stop raining soon they'll definitely cancel the barbecue tonight . . .'

'Mmm . . .'

Emma turned to look at her mum: 'A vanload of Martians have just arrived to take over our town!'

'Mmm . . .'

'Mum!' said Emma loudly. 'You're not listening!'

'What? . . . err . . . Oh, sorry . . . I was miles away.'

Emma grinned, 'Doesn't matter, I was just talking about the rain.' She flopped down next to her mum. Josie's tail gave a brief wag, then stopped, and the dog lowered her head back on to her paws with a sigh. Emma patted the soft black fur. 'She's not herself, is she?'

'Not at all . . .' Lynne gently stroked Josie's head. 'I've got a feeling that maybe it's starting . . .' As if in reply, Josie suddenly got to her feet and lumbered out of the room. A moment later they could hear her drinking noisily from her water dish.

Emma felt a bubble of excitement growing in her stomach. Josie was due to give birth to a litter of pups any day now. The family had thought of little else for weeks. 'I wish they'd come now!' she said, stretching out on the floor.

'You need to be more patient, Em; it could be a while yet.' Lynne got up. 'It's best just to keep busy . . .'

By teatime there was still no sign of the puppies. Josie was becoming more fretful – she paced the rooms, unable to settle in one position for any length of time. Emma watched her, wondering what the pups would be like. How many would there be? How would Josie cope with the birth? How would her family cope? They had no experience of puppies – or much of dogs! Josie was the family's first – and they'd only had her a little over a year.

Emma knelt down by Josie's side. The dog was sitting glumly in the hall now. 'It'll be all right, girl,' she said softly. 'I know it will.' She stroked Josie's sleek coat and the dog leaned against her. It was hard to believe that in a few hours' time Josie would be a mum.

It had been Lynne's idea to have Josie. Emma and her brother, Elliot, had been asking for a dog for years but it had never been the right time. Then Lynne heard about Guide Dogs and how they were looking for volunteers to help with the puppies. She briefly considered becoming a puppy walker (the person who cares for a guide dog puppy for the first year of its life), but she knew that she would never be able to give the dog up at the end of the year – and nor would the children. Then she heard about the families who cared for the female dogs who gave birth to the pups that would become guide dogs. Lynne immediately felt drawn to the idea, especially as they'd be allowed to keep the mum-dog forever; it would be a proper family pet and there would be puppies too! Understandably, the children were thrilled.

There were lots of arrangements to make before they got a dog. The family had to be carefully checked by Guide Dogs, to make sure that they were suitable. It was also important to find the best sort of dog to fit in with their family and their elderly cat, Misty.

Eventually, after several months, a match came through. Josie: a fourteen-month-old black Lab, who was being puppy trained by a cat-owning family with two boys the same age as Emma and Elliot. Josie sounded perfect, and when they went to meet her at the Guide Dog training centre a few weeks later, they instantly fell in love with her.

★

'Are you ready yet?' Emma's dad, Neil, appeared in the hall, followed by Elliot.

Emma shrugged, 'Maybe I should stay? You know . . . just in case Josie starts having her puppies.'

'It'll probably be a while yet,' said her dad. 'Anyway, your mum will be here . . . and you've been looking forward to the barbecue.'

'But it's raining!'

Elliot grinned. 'Then put on your wellies!'

Emma made a face; then, still laughing about rainy barbecues and soggy sausages, they headed off.

As the front door closed Lynne settled down with the paper and a cup of tea with Josie by her feet. But the dog couldn't settle – a few minutes later she was up again, padding around

101

the room, and now Lynne could see she was panting. Instinctively she felt it was time.

'Come on, girl,' she said softly, leading her to the whelping box. This was where she'd have her pups. Inside, everything was prepared – old newspapers, towels, plastic sheeting . . . all laid out ready. Lynne took a deep breath. This was it! She felt butterflies in her stomach. Here she was about to help bring a litter of puppies into the world and she'd never even had a dog before! She'd seen a birthing DVD of course, and Guide Dogs had explained what to expect, but nothing could really prepare you for what was about to happen. Lynne tried to keep her voice steady. Inside, her tummy was in knots, but she had to stay calm for Josie's sake. The dog seemed so confused and unsure of what was happening.

Just as the clock struck 7 p.m. it started. Josie suddenly stood up in the whelping box, muscle

contractions rippling down her belly, then she
went rigid, and Lynne spotted the first pup's head
appearing . . . She held her breath and watched
as the paws followed, and then in seconds the
tiny creature was out in the world, and Lynne
had to catch it. It felt so small in her hands, its
eyes and ears closed. Lynne carefully cleared the
pup's mouth and made sure it was breathing and
then for a second or two just looked in wonder
at the tiny pup. She rubbed it dry with a towel
and put it close to Josie. But they didn't have
long to recover. Soon another pup appeared and
then a third. This time Lynne's heart sank. The
pup wasn't breathing. She laid the tiny lifeless
little body down and felt a lump in her throat.
Nature could be so cruel.

Josie was tired now, she slid down on to the
floor of the box, still shaking and panting.

'Good girl, Josie, good girl . . .' said Lynne,

trying to keep her voice calm. She stroked the dog's head. Then when she was settled, Lynne gently moved the first two pups closer to her and helped them latch on to feed. Then she sat back on her heels to rest for a moment, as there would be more pups soon – she just hoped they'd be healthy.

The Guide Dogs' supervisor had visited the family weeks ago with an ultrasound machine, one similar to those used in hospitals for human babies. Lynne and the children had watched in wonder as the machine scanned Josie's belly, revealing half a dozen or so tiny pups not much bigger than jelly beans inside. It was hard to believe that was only weeks ago . . . and now here they were, being born in her kitchen.

For a while all was quiet. Josie rested fitfully and the first two pups slept. Lynne watched the clock and hoped everything would be all right.

The stillborn pup had been a shock – though she'd been warned it could happen. Soon the children would be back, and Lynne wasn't sure how they'd cope if the other pups didn't make it. She really wanted her children to share this experience and to witness the miracle of life and see another creature coming into the world.

Lynne looked down. Josie was alert again and panting quite heavily now. With much effort she hauled herself up on to her feet and her panting grew stronger. Another pup was coming. Lynne waited, praying this one would be alive. Then she saw a tiny head, and in seconds the fourth pup was out. Lynne caught it, and this time, thankfully, it *was* breathing. Just then the front door banged: Lynne's husband Neil and the children were home.

'Come in quietly,' she called. But she didn't really need to. The children understood. They were in awe of the scene. There was Josie, their beloved black dog, with three tiny bundles tucked up close beside her.

Elliot rested his chin on the edge of the box. His eyes wide like saucers. 'Good girl, Josie,' he breathed, softly stroking her head, 'good girl,' and then said to his mum: 'Will she have any more?'

Lynne nodded: 'Maybe another two or three . . .' For a second she considered not mentioning the dead pup. But somehow she knew the children would understand. 'She lost one, I'm afraid; it didn't make it. But hopefully the others will be OK.'

Emma gave her mum a squeeze, and to the dog she whispered, 'Poor Josie. Poor you . . .'

Both children were adamant they wanted to stay up and see the next pup being born. The hours passed, and there was still no sign of any

Archie

Snuggled up with Sean . . .

. . and also with Kate

Arthur

Alert in training

With his litter mates

With Andrea

Being the official ring-bearer
at Dawn and Neil's wedding

Gus

Brave Gus
and Jemma

Jamie

Jamie and Sidney on Centre
Court, Wimbledon

Emma with Jasper, one of
Josie's puppies

Josie's second litter

Josie

With Emma and Elliot

Raffles

Raffles with Lee and Lisa on their wedding day

Walking with Lee

Rags

With Fabian and in the staffroom

Shirley

Keeping watch over
Rebecca

Photo courtesy of Ben Lister

Photo courtesy of Damien McFadden

Trent

With Paul and Emily

more of the litter. Elliot grew weary. His eyes were shutting and when his dad scooped him up and carried him to bed the little lad didn't protest.

'I'm not going!' said Emma firmly. She brought down her duvet and snuggled down on the sofa, waiting for the next pup to come. Her dad wasn't so keen. He had work the next day and eventually headed off to bed.

'It's probably for the best,' Emma said, grinning. 'Dad's not so good with blood and yuk and stuff . . .'

Lynne smiled at her daughter and suddenly realized how much better she felt with Emma by her side. The responsibility of caring for Josie and the pups alone had been huge. Sharing a little of it with Emma made it feel much lighter.

They didn't have long to wait. Emma sat close by the box, her eyes wide with wonder.

She had to keep reminding herself to breathe: it was so exciting! Suddenly she saw the puppy's head appear – small and wet, and then its paws, and then the tiny bundle flopped out. Emma hadn't been sure what to expect; it was quite a bit messier than she imagined . . . but so much more amazing too! She'd actually witnessed the start of a new life. For a moment she couldn't speak, she just watched while her mum checked the pup's mouth was clear, then placed it carefully next to Josie. 'Wow,' breathed Emma. 'That was incredible . . .'

Lynne grinned. Her daughter's face was alight with wonder and awe. This was exactly the experience she'd hoped the kids would have. Something to remember forever.

Josie was exhausted now. She lay down and closed her eyes, still panting slightly, still shaking . . . The four pups squeaked slightly, and Lynne moved them closer to their mum.

Emma glanced at the clock. It was after 1 a.m. She'd never stayed up this late before. It felt like such an adventure. The minutes passed, then half an hour, then an hour . . . and there was still no sign of more pups. Emma started to grow weary, and so did Lynne. Her mum made some snacks to help them stay awake and they cuddled up on the sofa for a bit while the pups slept in a box and Josie rested by herself. Another hour dragged by, and then another, and still there were no new pups. Lynne began to worry. Surely it shouldn't take this long. She crouched close to Josie and ran her hand lightly along the dog's tummy. 'I'm sure I can feel more inside . . .'

'Is it bad that it's taking this long?' asked Emma, crouching close to them.

'I'm not sure . . . all births are different, but

I'm feeling a bit worried that Josie's getting too tired now.'

The dog lay on her side, still panting faintly, her eyes closed. Lynne felt a moment of fear sweep over her. If a pup got stuck inside her, it could be dangerous for both it and Josie.

'I'll call the supervisor,' she said. 'She'll know what to do.'

The supervisor shared Lynne's worries. She suggested Lynne call their local vet. Lynne made the call.

'He didn't seem overly worried,' she told Emma, when she came back into the room. 'He said we should let Josie sleep. . . .'

Emma looked down at the dog, who was still panting and shaking slightly.

'I'm not so sure,' said Lynne. 'It's been such a long time now . . .'

They had to get this right, thought Lynne.

Josie was special, really special. Up and down the country blind and partially sighted people were depending on her. Josie's pups would be the guide dogs of tomorrow.

Only the best dogs were chosen to have pups themselves. Not only did they have to have the perfect temperament: kind, gentle and eager to please. They also had to be the healthiest dogs. It wasn't just them that had to be the best: their own litter-mates and parents had to be the best too. If a brother or sister was found to have a slight health issue, or there was a problem with their temperament, then that dog would not be selected to become a 'mum-dog'. Producing top puppies was essential for the success of Guide Dogs. Looking down at Josie, panting and exhausted, Lynne suddenly felt the weight of responsibility resting on her shoulders. She had to make sure Josie and her pups were OK.

Instinct told her she must do something now.

Lynne called the supervisor again, and she in turn phoned the Guide Dogs' own vet, who asked them to bring Josie in to be examined.

So a little after 4 a.m., Lynne and Emma put on their coats, filled a hot-water bottle to keep the pups snug in their box on the journey, and then ventured out into the darkness. Exhausted as she was, Josie trotted after them obediently, climbing heavily into the back of the car. Lynne turned the heating up full blast to keep the pups warm and they set off.

'I can't believe it's still raining!' said Emma, hugging the puppy box close to her. It was pelting down: even with the windscreen wipers on full power, it was hard to see. It wasn't just the rain that was against them. Every traffic light they came to turned red. Lynne looked anxiously in her mirror and could see Josie lying in the back, her eyes closed.

'Come on!' she said, willing the lights to change to green . . . 'Come on!' The vet's surgery wasn't far, but every mile felt like twenty.

Half an hour later they were there: the pups still asleep in the box, Josie, on the table, being examined by the vet. 'There are still two pups in there,' the vet said after scanning her. 'But I can only see one heartbeat.'

Overwhelmed with tiredness, Lynne felt her shoulders sag. Emma tried not to cry.

'That might not mean anything,' the vet added quickly, 'it could be that I just can't see the other one properly . . . I'll give her an injection to restart the contractions, you can take her home and we'll see what happens.'

The vet had warned them that Josie might have a pup in the car on the way home. Emma, who was still clutching the pups in their box, kept a close eye on Josie but nothing happened.

It was still raining when they got home and Emma was so tired she could barely climb out of the car. 'Have a rest, love,' said her mum, tucking her up on the sofa.

'But I'll miss seeing the other puppies born,' she said, trying to fight off sleep. But it was impossible. It was after five in the morning, and as soon as her head touched the cushion Emma was asleep.

Meanwhile, Josie went back to the whelping box, panting and shivering as before. Weary herself, Lynne took up her position and less than an hour later another puppy was born. It was alive! She placed it next to its mum and began waiting patiently for the final pup to come. But it didn't appear. Time started dragging on. Josie was so tired she could barely stand.

Just after eight in the morning, the Guide

Dogs supervisor arrived at the house to check on Josie and the pups. She scanned Josie and could see a heartbeat. The last pup *was* alive too! But it needed to come out now – and Josie was too tired to do it. There was only one option left: an emergency caesarean section at the vet's.

Much later, when Emma finally opened her eyes, the sun was pouring in through the living-room window. She stretched and blinked a few times. For a moment she couldn't understand why she was there and not in her own bed . . . and then the night's excitement came flooding back.

'Josie? The pups?'

'They're fine.' Lynne appeared by the couch and sat down on the edge, smoothing Emma's hair away from her face. 'You did brilliantly last night. I'm so proud of you.'

'But what about the pups – were they both alive?'

'Yes. Josie had one here and the other at the vet's. They're all fine, and she's home already.'

Emma scrambled out from beneath the duvet. 'I have to see them!'

She found Elliot sitting by the whelping box, stroking the tiny creatures gently with his fingertips. 'The puppies are brilliant,' he beamed.

Emma grinned, then giggled. 'Yes, but, you know, the more I look at them, the more I think that they don't actually look like puppies yet, they're more like little fat sausages!'

At that, Elliot's tummy rumbled and everyone started to laugh . . . and even Josie sat up to see what the fuss was about.

After two weeks the pups opened their eyes.

They started eating solid food and stopped looking like little fat sausages and became much more puppy-like. By three weeks they'd started climbing out of their box, and by four weeks they were into everything: chewing, exploring and getting into all sorts of mischief. There were three girls and three boys – five black pups just like their mum, and one golden-coloured one.

Every litter of guide dog pups is given a letter of the alphabet and their names have to start with that letter. Josie's pups got the letter 'W'. So they were named: Wanda, Willow, Wallis, Wilson, Wesley and . . . Shearer. As life-long Newcastle fans Neil and Elliot had pleaded to name one of the boy pups after the Newcastle football legend Alan Shearer!

The kids loved having the pups to play with. The older they got, the more rascally they became – chewing slippers, escaping through the cat flap into the garden and getting under everyone's feet.

Lynne didn't mind. She loved the chaos. She also made sure the pups were handled often so that they could start building up their social skills. She introduced them to plenty of loud noise too – the vacuum cleaner, the washing machine – so that nothing would frighten them. Finally she held a 'Cuddle-a-puppy' fund-raising event, inviting friends and neighbours round to meet the pups and raised hundreds of pounds for Guide Dogs in the process.

All too soon the day came when the pups had to leave to start their puppy training. Lynne didn't try to hide her tears and neither did the kids. But the sadness was short-lived. Of course, they were sorry to see the pups go – they'd miss them – but they knew they were about to start an amazing journey. In less than two years all of the pups might be real, fully trained guide dogs, which seemed almost unbelievable when you looked at the tiny bundles of mischief tearing around Lynne's kitchen!

As she shut the door after the final pup had gone, it was Emma who, as usual, summed up the family's feelings perfectly. 'It's a bit like taking the Christmas decorations down,' she said glumly. 'Everything feels a bit flat and empty.'

Lynne hugged her daughter. 'It won't feel like this forever.'

And it didn't.

Two years later Josie went on to have a second litter. Again she had three girls and three boys — five black pups and one golden one. That was to be her final litter. Lynne kept a scrapbook all about her pups.

All but one of her first litter qualified as guide

dogs. When the second litter reached the puppy training stage the family decided to keep Lola, one of the pups, and walk her themselves. They knew they'd have to part with her someday soon, and that would be hard. They also knew they'd cope. The experience of having Josie and her pups had somehow changed them. They were part of the Guide Dogs team now – and they were ready to give Lola the best possible start on her journey to becoming a guide dog. After all, they would always have Josie, their kind-hearted, gentle black Labrador – and they could care for and cuddle her forever.

Raffles

The football thumped over the fence, landing right under Raffle's nose. For a second or two the dog tried to ignore it . . . but he just couldn't help himself. He pounced on the ball, grabbing it in his mouth excitedly, his tail banging against the ground with joy.

'Raffles?'

He paused at the sound of his name, but quickly went back to his game – pushing the ball away with his nose before pouncing on it again.

'Come on now, Raffles, give it back to me . . .' Lee Greatbatch – his owner – had appeared now, and was not amused: 'We've got a football game going on here!'

Raffles wasn't interested. He just rolled around on his tummy, with the ball tucked under his paws . . .

Lee sighed. It was always the same when Raffles got a hold of a football; he never gave it back willingly. Lee bent down and wrestled it out of Raffles's grip. 'You're a very silly dog!' he said, trying to sound stern. 'Now settle down and stay out of mischief.'

Lee turned to go back to the game, and Raffles gave a bark. 'None of that nonsense either!' he said, trying not to smile.

Raffles lay down then and put his head on his paws. He knew it wasn't the best behaviour for a top-notch guide dog – especially not one who belonged to an international sportsman, but when it came to football, he just couldn't help himself.

★

Raffles had been with Lee for eight years now. During that time, he'd been Lee's constant companion. Lee had a busy life. He played blind football at league and international level. He also ran his own business. This meant that Raffles was used to adapting quickly to new situations and people. He was a friendly dog – a big black Labrador with a shiny coat and velvety ears. He loved people, especially children, but it was football that he got really excited about. Probably because he spent so much time around the game.

Lee had started playing blind football at school. Now, ten years on, he'd won fifty caps for his country and represented Great Britain in the 2008 Olympic Games in Beijing. It hadn't been easy. Becoming a top paralympian had involved a lot of training and hard work and as far as Lee was concerned he couldn't have done it without Raffles. The dog escorted Lee to the gym every day so he could train and keep fit. Then there were the trips to the football ground for frequent practice sessions. All of it would have been so much harder without the freedom and independence that Raffles brought him.

Lee was an inspirational young man in many ways. He'd never let his sight loss stop him from doing what he wanted. He was determined and focused, full of positive energy.

It was these skills that led Lee to a local primary school. Encouraging others to play sport was something he was passionate about, so when he'd been asked to coach a class of seven-year-olds he'd jumped at the chance. The primary school that had invited him in also wanted Lee to mentor one boy in particular: Harrison, who was blind, just like Lee himself.

'Go ahead, you can stroke Raffles . . .'

It was Lee's first day at the school, and he was introducing himself and his dog to the children. Harrison liked dogs, and he was enjoying being close to Raffles. He stroked the dog's shiny coat and smiled; it felt soft and silky. He stroked the dog's head too, and Raffles's tail began to wag.

'His ears are like velvet,' said Harrison.

Lee gave Raffles a pat. 'Yes, and he loves a bit of a fuss.'

Raffles certainly did! He was an affectionate dog, kind and patient, with a slight mischievous twinkle in his eyes. Normally when he was on duty he couldn't let himself be distracted by other people. But today was different.

'Would anyone else like to stroke Raffles?' Lee asked.

Twenty-eight voices shouted: 'Me!' Lee grinned. Raffles was a great ice-breaker.

Wherever he went people were always interested in the dog and that was especially true today. Harrison gave him another pat, and Raffles's tail wagged even harder.

Being the only blind pupil in the school was sometimes a challenge for Harrison, and sports were even more of a challenge. Lee was there to show him, and his classmates, that sight loss wasn't a barrier to taking part, or indeed, excelling in sport.

Before they started playing football, Lee wanted to tell the children a bit about himself and his guide dog.

'When Raffles is off duty he's just like an ordinary dog,' explained Lee. 'He's nosy and funny and gets up to all sorts of mischief. He especially likes to stick his nose in other people's shopping bags! Or sports bags – or anything else he can find.'

Raffles wagged his tail cheerfully, and his ears pricked up. He always knew when people were talking about him and he loved it!

'Once I put on his harness,' said Lee, 'all that changes. He becomes quiet and dependable: a true professional. He helps me to travel on trains and buses, through towns and cities and along busy roads. He makes sure I don't bump into lamp-posts or pillar boxes and he helps me to cross busy roads.'

'How does Raffles know which way to go?' asked one of the children.

Lee smiled: 'He doesn't really, I have to tell him, though he's very clever and once he's travelled a particular route a few times he usually remembers it for next time. The more he does a route the more he remembers it, like when he take me to football practice he knows exactly where the train station is, where he should cross

127

the road and when to turn left or right. I don't have to keep reminding him.'

'What about when you're crossing a road,' asked a boy, 'how do you know when it's safe if you can't see the cars?'

'By listening carefully! Also, Raffles is trained not to step out in front of traffic, so he always keeps me safe. Some people think guide dogs also know when the green man appears on a pedestrian crossing, but unfortunately that's not true. The owner still has to make the final decision, but always with their guide dog's help, of course.'

'Can I stroke him?' a girl asked. Raffles immediately started wagging his tail again.

'You definitely can today,' said Lee. 'But if you ever see a guide dog on the streets working with its owner it's best to ask the owner first because sometimes when people make a fuss of a guide dog it can be a bit of a distraction. Both the dog and the owner have to concentrate really hard to stay safe and remember the route they're taking so it's very important to ask first.'

'You are so lucky, Harrison!' said one of the boys sitting near him. 'One day you'll probably have a really cool dog like Raffles!'

Lee nodded: 'Raffles is amazing. All guide dogs are. Raffles is like my eyes. He gives me the freedom to go out and do everything I want to.'

Lee had already achieved a lot. He'd lost his sight when he was seven from a condition called glaucoma and he'd spent most of his childhood in foster care. Despite the challenges he'd faced, he'd always been a determined young man. With the support and encouragement of his foster family he did well at school, went on to college, and then to university. Along the way he started playing blind football and discovered that he had a real talent for the sport. Raffles came into his life soon after and after a lot of hard work and practice, Lee started playing football for England.

'OK, this is the ball we're going to use today. As you can hear it's got ball-bearings inside – which means it rattles when it moves.' Lee held the ball up and gave it a shake. The children gazed at it in awe. 'The noise the ball makes allows a blind footballer to hear it and keep track of it.'

It was the start of Lee's coaching sessions. Harrison and the rest of his class were listening intently as Lee explained the rules of blind football.

'There are five players in each team. Four are blind and the goalkeeper is sighted. In real football tournaments the blind players all wear blindfolds or eye-patches, because some might have a small amount of vision so the blindfolds keep it fair.'

The children were chattering with excitement now, desperate to have a go. Lee held his hand up for quiet: 'Now, remember, if you're not involved in the game, if you're waiting for your turn to play you need to stay silent so that the players can hear the ball and each other while they're playing. Being able to listen properly is crucial!'

Everyone settled down then, and Lee divided the children into teams. Two players in each team were blindfolded while the other three could still see. This was so there was less chance of them bumping into each other and getting hurt. Then it was time for the first games to begin.

Lee was impressed. The children took to the game quickly. They were enthusiastic and excited, but they didn't find it easy. Once they'd started playing they realized how important listening was and also that they had to talk to one another clearly and communicate well so that they could keep track of the ball and each other!

Soon it was Harrison's turn. Football was something he'd never thought he'd be able to play. Now suddenly he could. He was excited and a little nervous — understandably so — football wasn't something he'd tried before, but he loved it from the start.

Blind football involves a lot of close-contact dribbling of the ball as the players keep the ball moving constantly so they can hear it. It's faster than ordinary football, too, and the ball is heavier — so that it can't bounce so high.

Many of the children in Harrison's class who were used to playing sighted football found the game hard. They weren't used to having to listen so carefully or to keeping the ball close by them.

At first, Harrison found it hard too, but by the end of the first session he was moving more freely and working well with the ball. After a few more sessions he was starting to pass confidently. He was talking to his team-mates too, telling them when he was going for the ball or passing it to them. For a boy who'd never thought he could play football, it was an exciting experience. His enthusiasm for the game went home with him and his parents even got him a ball of his own to practise with.

When the coaching sessions ended Lee was asked to stay on at the school as a part-time teaching assistant to work with Harrison. As the months passed Harrison's enthusiasm for sport grew. He was participating more in PE lessons, and he kept up his football practice too. He was becoming a strong swimmer. Before Lee came, Harrison was already an outgoing, friendly boy who enjoyed being with people. Now, with his interest in sport, his independence was growing even more.

After a year it was time for Lee to move on. During his time in the school he hoped he'd shown Harrison that with the help of a guide dog and a bit of hard work and determination, he could do anything he wanted: play sport, go to college or university and be a success at anything he tried – perhaps even become a paralympian. When he'd started at the school Lee had given Harrison some Olympic souvenirs, including a football strip he'd worn and a badge he'd brought back from the Games.

Later that day, as Harrison walked home with his dad he told him about his new plan:

'When I'm a teenager, I'd like a guide dog just like Raffles.'

In many ways, Raffles was the key to Lee's success. As a footballer he was signed up to West Bromwich Albion football club and travelled weekly to the Hawthorns stadium for evening training sessions. Without Raffles it would have been difficult for him to make that journey.

Raffles also helped Lee when he backed a campaign to encourage more schoolchildren to walk to school. To launch the campaign Lee and Raffles walked to school with a group of children to show them that it was not only a good way to keep fit, but also great fun. Raffles, as always, loved being in the middle of it all and the children thought it was particularly cool to have a dog walk them to school. Raffles was becoming a bit of a star!

Indeed, Raffles was always at the heart of things. When Lee got married Raffles was involved in the big day too. Lisa, Lee's wife, had wanted the dog to wear a posh coat for the day, but Lee wasn't keen. 'He's already got a lovely coat!' he protested. Lee relented and Raffles wore a pink bow-tie to match the groom, best man and the ushers. Raffles loved it. He was looked after by a friend at the wedding and because he was off duty he made the most of all the fuss and attention he got from the other wedding guests.

Raffles was a very special dog. Whatever Lee was doing with his life, he was always on hand to support him and help him. In many ways he was Lee's best friend, as he proved again just a few months after the wedding.

It was a Sunday evening and Lisa and Lee were in the living room watching telly. Raffles couldn't settle; he kept pacing the floor and running back and forward to the kitchen, whining. Lee thought he must have wanted out to go out, but he didn't. Eventually Lee followed him into the kitchen, only to find Raffles sitting next to the oven. Lee could smell gas, and then he heard the hissing. The gas hob had been left on, unlit, with gas leaking out. It was a lucky escape. Leaking gas could have caused an explosion or a fire. Raffles had sensed the danger and alerted them, showing yet again what a bright and helpful dog he was. Not that Lee needed any reminding. As he and Lisa made a huge fuss of Raffles, Lee hugged him close, breathing in the familiar scent of his silky coat and the warmth of his familiar bulk. Lee led such a busy life; it was nice to know there was always someone watching over him.

★

It was a dark night in January and Lee's latest football training session had just ended. He was tired. It had been a long day: work first, and then a train journey, followed by two hours of football practice − including the little incident with Raffles and the ball! As he picked up Raffles's harness to head home, he chuckled softly to himself. To look at Raffles now, the picture of professionalism, carefully escorting his owner through the dark streets down to the train station, you'd never know there was a football-crazy puppy lurking deep inside! Lee chuckled again. The truth was, Raffles wasn't so different to Lee . . . Theirs was indeed the perfect partnership.

Rags

It was growing dark now. But Rags still didn't move. He lay in the same place on the hall floor. His head was resting on his paws, his eyes were fixed on the front door, but still there was no sign of his owner returning. It was all so confusing. Why didn't he come back?

Rags was a long-haired retriever cross, with a shaggy black coat, soft, friendly eyes and a waggy tail. For the past three years he'd been guide dog to an elderly gentleman. They'd suited one another well; both quiet, both calm. Then everything had suddenly changed. His owner had got ill and today he'd been taken to hospital in an ambulance, leaving Rags alone.

For a dog that was used to going everywhere with his owner – escorting him safely on every journey – it was strange to be left by himself.

As the clock chimed the hour, Rags heard footsteps in the distance, faint at first but growing louder as they approached the front door. Rags knew they didn't belong to his owner. He sat up, alert, and watched as a key turned in the lock, and then a friendly face appeared. 'Hello, Rags,' the man said. 'I've come to fetch you . . .'

It was three weeks later and Rags was living with one of the Guide Dogs staff. His elderly owner had never recovered, sadly, and passed away. The problem now was: what would they do with Rags? At just five years old he was too young to retire, but he was also too old to be given to a new owner. Many families would have wanted him as a pet, but Rags was a working dog. Years of training had given him the skills to help people and the team at Guide Dogs were keen for him to continue doing just that.

A new scheme seemed to hold the answer: buddy dogs! It was an idea that Guide Dogs were testing – placing dogs in special schools and residential care homes to become companion dogs. The scheme would give some residents and pupils the chance to find out what it would be like to have their own guide dog. For others there would be the therapeutic benefits of just being around a dog.

The dogs involved in the project were either close to retiring, like Rags, or those that hadn't quite made it as guide dogs, but had many of the skills and the right temperament. The scheme seemed ideal for Rags. Arrangements were made and within the month he had a new job.

★

'Not far now, Rags. Two more stops and we'll be there . . .'

It was a sunny morning in the first week of September and Rags was on the bus, on his way to RNIB Pears Centre for Specialist Learning. With him was Louise Ashton, who worked at the school, and who had volunteered to be Rags's carer when he was off-duty.

'This is our stop.' Louise gathered up her coat and bag, and Rags was already standing patiently by her side, his guide dog training shining through. As they stepped off the bus Rags seemed to have a spring in his step, almost as though he knew he was working again and was glad to be back on duty.

RNIB Pears Centre taught and cared for children and young people who had both sight loss and other disabilities too. When Guide Dogs had asked if they'd like to take part in the buddy-dog scheme and have a dog for a year to see if it helped their students they were keen to give it a go.

Louise was anxious for the scheme to work. She was an experienced dog-owner herself and she'd grown up with dogs. She'd always had one of her own and she passionately believed dogs were good for children. She just hoped the rest of the school would see that too.

'Here we are now.' Louise took a deep breath, then pressed the buzzer. The school door swung open. Rags had arrived.

The children at the school were mostly teenagers. All of them were blind or partially sighted. They also had learning difficulties, and most had other disabilities too. Some couldn't walk or move around freely. Others found it hard to communicate or interact with other people.

Despite the difficulties and challenges the young people faced the school was not a sad place. In fact, it was completely the opposite! The school was warm and encouraging, a happy and exciting place to be, where young people could reach and exceed their goals. Just like any school, the walls were brightly decorated with pictures, projects and photos of the students taking part in their lessons. There was a student council, swimming lessons and a chance to unwind and relax together at school parties and outings.

It was a small school and, although most of the students also lived there, a handful were day pupils who went home after lessons ended. Fabian was one such pupil.

Karen Gannon, the deputy head of the school, had thought of Fabian as soon as she'd heard about buddy dogs. Fabian was fifteen years old and had been blind since birth. He was also autistic, which meant he found it hard to interact and communicate with others. He struggled to empathize with people and to know how they were feeling or what they were thinking. Fabian also found it very hard to imagine things, and for a blind person that was a huge difficulty. He had never been close to a dog before, and having someone describe a dog to him was useless because he was unable to create a picture of one in his mind. Instead, he had to rely on instinct and his senses: touch, smell, sound.

Fabian's classroom was one of the first places Rags visited. Karen and the teachers watched closely for Fabian's reaction. It was good – he was immediately interested. At the start, Rags's visits to the classrooms were brief. The students might not be able to see Rags, but they could hear his breathing. They could touch his thick shaggy coat, and they could certainly smell him!

Some of the children were wary of him, and others weren't interested in him at all.

The school had agreed to have Rags for a year. During that time, the effect on the students would be monitored constantly. What would he bring to the school? A few of the teachers wondered if he'd contribute anything valuable at all. Others were more encouraging; they felt having a dog would be good for morale, both for the students and staff. Some felt it was worth doing simply because it was a new experience and out of the ordinary. Karen was also hoping the children would benefit from being able to look after Rags, to take responsibility for him, to groom him, to care for him and to walk him. And that was where Fabian came in.

'What does his coat feel like, Fabian?' Karen was sitting with some of the students while they got to know Rags.

Fabian stroked his fur, running his hand down the side of the dog, then back up to his head for another stroke.

'He's enjoying the fuss,' Karen said, and laughed. 'Listen to his tail wagging!'

Of all the students, Fabian seemed to enjoy Rags's company the most. Karen suspected this was partly because he was more mobile than most of the others. Although he often needed support, Fabian could walk, and Karen was hoping that Rags, as a former guide dog, might give Fabian more independence and confidence. Eventually she hoped that Rags might even allow Fabian to move around the school and its grounds on his own. But that would be a huge step for Fabian. To do it, he would have to be able to take control of the dog, tell it when to stop, sit down, walk on and turn left or right.

He'd also have to react swiftly to new situations, and because of his autism this was particularly difficult for him to do.

Fabian was enthusiastic and interested in learning. He followed instructions well. He thrived on routine. He had even started working at the school's reception desk on Thursday mornings, answering the door buzzer and helping with typing and filing. Fabian was able to do all of that because it had a set pattern to it. When he answered the door buzzer, he knew what to say. What Fabian struggled with was situations that were unplanned or unexpected, and those were exactly what he would face if he took charge of Rags.

A few months later Fabian got his chance to try.

Alfie Wilson, one of the staff members, appeared in the doorway and announced: 'I'm going to put Rags on his lead now, Fabian, and then you're going to have a go at walking him yourself, OK?'

Fabian immediately stood up. He was ready for it. During the past few weeks he'd regularly accompanied staff members as they walked the dog around the school or outside in the grounds. Now it was his turn to take control. Rags – ever patient – stood calmly by Fabian's side while he took up the lead. Together they walked down the corridor, turned left, and then went down the next corridor. At first, Rags was obviously in charge with Fabian following silently by his side. But by the third trip around the building Fabian was beginning to look more relaxed and more confident.

'Come on now . . . don't forget to give Rags some instruction . . .' Alfie was following a few paces behind, encouraging and supporting them both. Then Rags caught the scent of something interesting on the ground and hesitated for a second. Alfie was about to remind Fabian to take control, when . . . 'Walk on,' said Fabian quietly. Then Fabian said 'Walk on!' again, more loudly that time. And Rags did.

What Fabian was doing might sound easy to many of us. But it wasn't. Walking Rags was forcing Fabian to react and think for himself. There was no set text for him to follow. There was no routine to stick to. If Rags slowed down, or turned the wrong way, or got distracted, then it was down to Fabian alone to correct him. And he did. The more he practised, the louder and more confident he became. It was a huge step forward for Fabian, but the success or failure of the buddy-dog scheme at the school couldn't just rest on his shoulders. For Rags to be truly useful he would have to bring something to the lives of the other students too.

As weeks, then months passed, there were more successes. Small steps, but for the children involved, very important ones. There was the day when a young girl, who was usually reluctant to be close to Rags, actually reached out her hand to cautiously touch the metal name disc that jangled on his collar.

Then there was the morning when another child, who felt uncomfortable touching anything with her hands, gently inched forward in her wheelchair to allow her elbow to brush softly against Rags's fur, smiling as she did so.

Karen felt there were others who could benefit too. Mobility was a big challenge for many students at the school. Some of the students who spent much of their time in wheelchairs were reluctant to do their exercises and to practise walking. Karen was hopeful that eventually

Rags might be able to encourage them to walk more – after all, walking is much more fun when you're doing it with a dog by your side.

As the months passed, Rags became a much-loved member of the school team. Although a few staff members were still doubtful of the benefits he brought, most felt that he boosted staff morale too. After a challenging lesson Rags was always ready to greet you with a wag of his tail and a friendly twinkle in his eye. He became a familiar sight at Reception, where he waited until he was needed. When school finished Louise would collect him, and together they'd catch the bus home.

'Do you think Rags will stay?'

It was a question Louise hated asking of the deputy head. She desperately wanted him to.

Not only did Louise enjoy looking after the big, gentle dog – in truth she'd fallen for him the first day she met him – she'd also seen for herself the positive effect he'd had on some of the students. Louise believed strongly that pets always improved a child's wellbeing. Seeing Rags at school just reinforced her views.

Karen smiled. 'I don't know,' she said. 'At the moment we've only got him for a year. Then we'll have to get together with Guide Dogs and decide whether the buddy-dog scheme has worked for us.'

Louise already felt it had and so did Fabian's mum, Jacqui. She had heard all about her son's work with Rags and saw it as yet another huge achievement brought about by the school. Since Fabian had started there seven years ago, she'd seen him grow in confidence and achieve so much – well beyond even her own expectations.

153

The question of whether Rags stayed at the school was one to address later on, but for now Fabian and some of the other students would carry on working with him, growing in confidence and gaining more independence. There was even an idea, that someday, much further in the future, Fabian might even have a guide dog of his own. Rags, the shaggy-coated warm-hearted friend to all, had brought a richness to school life. He truly was a buddy dog.

Shirley

It was hot in the room but seven-year-old Rebecca didn't notice. She was too caught up in the music. It was a children's disco and, like most girls her age, Rebecca loved to dance. She waved to her mum, Claire, as another song started. Claire smiled back – it was good to see her daughter enjoying herself. They were on holiday in Cornwall: a chance for the whole family to unwind and relax. They needed it.

Rebecca suffered from an aggressive form of diabetes. This illness meant her body couldn't control its sugar levels. It was a life-threatening condition; at any moment Rebecca could suffer a hypoglycaemic attack – when her sugar levels would drop dangerously low and she would slip into unconsciousness. It happened all too regularly: that heart-stopping moment when she'd pass out and her mum would have to frantically call the paramedics to revive her. As a result, Claire watched Rebecca constantly and was terrified that she would miss the warning signals of an attack. Thankfully, today her little girl looked well; her cheeks were rosy and she was happily bounding around the dance floor, joining in with her new friends.

Then Claire felt a touch on her hand. It was Shirley, their Labrador dog, and in her mouth was Rebecca's sugar-testing kit. For a second Claire's stomach tightened, and then she jumped up. 'Rebecca!' she called. 'Come over here, please . . .'

Reluctant to leave the dance floor, Rebecca walked over slowly. She had spotted the blood-sugar testing kit in her mum's hand. She didn't like it. To test her sugar levels, to make sure they were normal, her mum had to take a tiny pinprick of blood from Rebecca's thumb. It didn't hurt much: but, understandably, Rebecca didn't like it. She knew it was important though – it kept her alive.

As another song began, Rebecca was itching to get back on the dance floor but Claire kept her close, waiting for the result. It was 2.3 – dangerously low. Sugar levels of less than five were too low; over fifteen would be too high. Rebecca was moments away from having a hypo attack.

'Drink this, Rebecca, quick as you can.' Claire handed her a can of sugary drink. Rebecca urgently needed to boost her sugar levels. Obediently, Rebecca started to drink and while she did, Claire turned to Shirley, the Labrador and held her close. 'Good girl,' she whispered in the dog's ear. 'Thank you.' Amazingly Shirley had known that Rebecca's life was in danger, and she'd alerted Rebecca's mum just in time. Most dogs couldn't have done it, but Shirley was no ordinary dog. She was a life-saving medical-alert dog. She was trained to detect when Rebecca's sugar levels were too high or too low, simply by sniffing a change in Rebecca's scent that occurred when her sugar levels went up or down. Somehow, from across the busy dance floor, the dog had sensed Rebecca was in danger and had acted quickly. She'd saved Rebecca's life – again!

'Drink a bit more . . .' Claire watched Rebecca closely, making sure she had drunk enough to boost her sugar levels properly. . . Shirley kept close too. Watching and waiting, making sure Rebecca was safe. She always did. She was

Rebecca's constant companion. She even went to school with her. She slept by her bed at night and whenever she noticed a change in Rebecca's scent she would urgently lick the girl's hands to alert her, or fetch her mum. Shirley had already saved Rebecca's life dozens of times, and since they'd had her, Claire hadn't had to call the paramedics at all. Without Shirley, Rebecca wouldn't have been able to do all the normal things most children take for granted . . . like dancing.

'Can I go now?' Rebecca wiped her lips and grinned at her mum. 'I feel fine now.'

Claire smiled. Rebecca had been just seconds away from a hypo attack, and now, thanks to Shirley, she was safe again and ready to go back to being an ordinary little girl.

The journey that had brought Shirley into

Rebecca's life had started more than a year ago when the dog had been training to be a guide dog. She was a bright and playful pup, very loving and full of fun. However, her walker had been concerned for some time that she might not have all the qualities needed to be a guide dog. She had the perfect temperament: gentle and affectionate, and she was clever too — but she sometimes got distracted when she was out on a walk and that was something a guide dog couldn't do.

Then, just a few weeks before the end of Shirley's walking training, her trainer happened to hear a talk given by the charity Medical Detection Dogs. This is a group who train dogs to use their noses to sniff out and detect and alert their owners that they are about to become ill. They do this by noticing a tiny change in their owner's smell when they are becoming poorly.

Shirley

A change so small that a human nose would never notice it. The subject was of particular interest to Shirley's walker because she had diabetes herself – just like Rebecca. She'd noticed that whenever her own sugar levels changed slightly, Shirley would become agitated, as though she sensed it. This gave her an idea. She knew the charity was always looking for bright dogs to train and she thought Shirley might be suitable. And she was! Although she wouldn't become a guide dog – Shirley was about to start an equally important job: one that saved lives.

'OK, now Shirley – let's try this one . . .'

It was a few months later and Shirley was in the middle of her training to become a medical-alert dog. She was doing well. She had a strong interest in scent, which made training her much easier and quicker than with many dogs. Today she was being trained with scent pots – tiny containers that had different smells inside. When she correctly noticed a change in the smells – and then alerted her trainer to the change – she was rewarded.

A lady called Claire Guest, who worked for Medical Detection Dogs, was overseeing Shirley's progress. She was pleased to see how much the dog seemed to enjoy the training. It was as though Shirley thought of it as a fun game. Shirley was a bright and inquisitive dog, but, more than that, she also had a strong personality, strong enough to be able to alert her trainer when she noticed a change in the smells. That was the vital skill she needed – to communicate what she sensed.

In a matter of weeks Shirley was ready and Claire had one person in mind for her . . . a little girl named Rebecca.

★

Rebecca had been four when she'd first become ill. She'd contracted a virus which had attacked her pancreas, leaving her with a life-threatening illness: diabetes. As Rebecca was so young, it was difficult for her to manage the condition. She could be feeling fine one minute, playing with her twin brother Joseph, or watching television, and then moments later a hypo attack would strike and she'd be slipping into unconsciousness. The strain on her mum was enormous. Claire couldn't sleep at night. She would lie awake, listening out for any sounds from Rebecca because she was terrified that she'd miss Rebecca having an attack while she slept.

Rebecca was a brave child: she put up with a lot, not least having to have four insulin injections a day. Insulin is a hormone produced by the pancreas which helps the body to absorb sugar from food, which it needs for energy. Rebecca's pancreas no longer produced insulin because of the virus she'd contracted, so she had to have injections every day.

'Hello there . . . can we come in?'

It was Shirley and Rebecca's first meeting to see if they would hit it off. They definitely did!

'Awww – she's lovely!' Rebecca immediately wrapped her arms around the Labrador's neck and hugged her close. 'Can I take her home now?'

It had been Rebecca's uncle who'd first heard about medical-alert dogs. He'd seen an advert in the paper looking for foster homes for the dogs while they were being trained. He showed it to Rebecca's mum, not so that they could foster a dog in training, but so she could apply for one to keep Rebecca safe.

Shirley

The charity was keen to help, but staff said that Rebecca would need a very special dog because she was so young. It would have to be gentle and not too lively. Rebecca was small, so the dog couldn't be one that might be too boisterous or knock her over. Shirley, with the gentleness gained from her guide dog training, seemed ideal. Two weeks after they first met her, Shirley came to live with Rebecca and her family.

'Remember, it will take a few weeks before she can fully help you,' warned Claire. 'She needs time to get to know your scent before she can start alerting you properly.'

Shirley spent so much time with Rebecca that she got to recognize her smell quickly. Within two weeks she had started alerting the family to any change in the little girl's smell. Shirley would go to Rebecca first, licking the girl's hands and feet and, if she ignored her, Shirley would find Rebecca's mum. The family might be anywhere when it happened – in the park, at the shops, in the street, or visiting friends. Shirley was always alert.

For Claire, it was a huge relief. She immediately felt a weight had been taken off her shoulders. Finally, after two years of broken sleep and constant anxiety, she could rest a little easier. Shirley was now on constant watch. 'It's amazing – a bit like having Lassie live with us!' Claire told a friend. 'Before she came, Rebecca would collapse three or four times a week. Now Shirley's here, that's all changed. Rebecca's so much better.'

Shirley didn't just keep Rebecca safe; she also became her best friend. The pair were inseparable. If they weren't playing together, they'd usually be curled up together, day and night. There was only one place Shirley didn't go at first, and that was school.

It was a sunny day, not long after Shirley had arrived. Rebecca, as usual, had kissed the dog goodbye at the school gates – leaving her with her mum for the day. Then it had been lessons, PE and an afternoon story. Rebecca had seemed fine for most of the day, but an hour before home time, she'd quickly become ill. Her face turned pale. Her legs went wobbly. She was weak and tired-looking. Her head ached and she was confused. She rapidly began to slip into a dangerous sleep. Her teachers acted quickly, and, thankfully, were able to revive her, just before the paramedics arrived. But for Rebecca's headmaster, it was too close for comfort.

A few days later, after Rebecca had returned

to class, the headmaster took her mum to one side and asked whether they could consider letting Shirley accompany Rebecca into class each day. Claire thought it was a good idea, but before it could happen there was a lot of work to be done. After all, they would be making history; this would be the first time a medical-alert dog had been used in a mainstream school!

First of all, the headmaster wrote to all the parents to make sure they were happy with a dog being in the classroom. Then Rebecca's teachers had to be trained. Claire Guest from Medical Detection Dogs visited the school several times to work with them and to get everything ready for the start of the following term. After weeks of preparation, the big day finally arrived.

It was the first day of school after the summer holidays, a day that no one at the school would forget. As the children lined up to go inside, there was a new classmate in the queue: Shirley! The children were very excited and everyone wanted to stand next to Rebecca.

'Your dog's so cool!' said one boy, giving Shirley a stroke.

'I wish I had a dog like her . . .' said another.

'She's so special!' said a girl.

Shirley *was* special and so was Rebecca. After all, not everyone got to take their best friend to school! Their teacher had explained to the children how Shirley helped Rebecca, so the children knew how important the dog was for her. But all the same, it was great fun to have a dog in class, especially one like Shirley.

Despite the attention she got, Shirley was very well behaved. Her guide dog training had taught her to be calm and gentle at all times; she was also soft and friendly and loved being with the children. Most importantly, she got straight to work and quickly started alerting the teachers whenever Rebecca's sugar levels were changing. If they dropped too low, a teaching assistant would give Rebecca something sweet to eat or drink. If her levels were too high she'd need an insulin injection.

As the weeks turned into months, it was as if Shirley had always been part of Rebecca's family. Claire couldn't remember how they'd coped without her. Rebecca had far fewer hypo attacks. She no longer had to be rushed to hospital regularly. She was also more confident and outgoing – just like she'd been before the illness.

It wasn't just Rebecca who had benefited from Shirley's arrival. Her mum felt like a dark cloud had been blown away from above her too. Now she was able to share the worry of keeping

Rebecca safe with someone else she could enjoy life much more herself.

And as more people got to hear about Shirley's remarkable abilities, the dog became a bit of a star. She and Rebecca appeared in newspapers and on national television. People stopped them in the street; everyone wanted to know about the amazing dog who kept the little girl safe. Shirley took all the attention in her stride. There was only one thing she was interested in and that was Rebecca. Somehow Shirley instinctively knew that Rebecca was poorly and needed looking after. Right from the day she arrived, she was never happier than when she was by the little girl's side, watching over her carefully.

It was February and Rebecca and her family had just heard that Shirley had been selected as a finalist by Crufts – the top dog show – in the 'Friend for Life' category. Later, after Claire had tucked Rebecca into bed for the night and turned off her light, she glanced back. Rebecca was already curled up and dropping off to sleep, her little face peaceful and untroubled. Next to her bed, curled up in her basket, was Shirley. The dog's head was turned towards Rebecca, as always, keeping a close eye on her young charge. Claire smiled. Shirley didn't need to win at Crufts. To them the dog was already a friend for life. In fact, she was more than that. She was like a guardian angel, keeping a constant vigil over their Rebecca.

Trent

Paul Cutress was lost now, he was sure of that. For a moment or two he felt a cloud of anxiety pass over him. Then he took a deep breath. *Surely there wasn't supposed to be a crossing here — was there?* He reached down to Trent, his guide dog. 'I hope you know where we are, boy, because I haven't got a clue!' The dog just wagged his tail in reply.

Then Devon Gidley, his guide dog mobility instructor, stepped in: 'Don't worry, Paul — you're doing really well.'

Paul didn't feel like he was doing well. He felt like he was failing — fast. As though he was on a driving test and he'd just bumped the car up a kerb.

'I just wish Trent didn't walk so fast,' sighed Paul. 'I don't have time to think about the route when I'm moving that quickly.'

'You'll get the hang of it, and there's no rush . . .' Devon said, and smiled. 'We'll keep practising until you do.'

Paul shook his head. Sometimes he didn't think he'd ever be able to do it. But he had to. He needed to make this work, to be more independent – to be able to get around by himself. There was also Emily to consider.

Emily was Paul's seven-year-old daughter. For the past few months, she'd been growing ever closer to Trent, the guide dog who had come to live with them while Paul did his training. If he didn't qualify as a guide dog owner, Trent would have to leave the family forever and Paul wasn't sure how Emily would cope with that.

'Come on now,' said Devon. 'I think we've

done enough for today – let's head back . . .' She gently steered Paul and Trent in the direction for home. 'You *will* get there, Paul, I know you will.'

Paul wished he had the same faith in himself that Devon seemed to have.

Trent had arrived one cold November day. Paul hadn't been sure quite what to expect; he'd never owned a dog before. At first Trent was quiet. Everything in the house was new and unfamiliar to him. He took a while to settle – he was off his food and moped around the house looking sad. Gradually, he began to cheer up, taking a particular shine to young Emily.

Trent was a big, black dog – a gentle, curly-coated retriever cross. He had a white patch on his chest and twinkly eyes. Emily loved him from the start, and they soon became great playmates. Paul was more wary. He liked Trent well enough, but he was apprehensive about beginning his guide dog training. Paul had tried the training before, but it hadn't worked out. Now – ten years on – he was about to start again. Understandably, he felt nervous about it.

'Morning, Paul, are you ready?' It was the first week of Paul's training and Devon was on his doorstep bright and early. They had a lot to do.

Devon had matched Paul and Trent together. She'd chosen the dog for him because he was solid and dependable, but also happy-go-lucky – a real personality dog. Devon knew Trent well. When he'd finished his basic guide dog training it was she who had taken him on to 'finish him off', skills-wise. This involved ten weeks of advanced training where Trent's skills were specially tailored to suit Paul's needs. When

Devon had first taken Trent to meet Paul, they'd hit it off well. They had an instant rapport. It looked like they'd work well together. After a further two weeks of training with Devon, Trent finally moved in with Paul and Emily. Now it was Paul's turn to start learning.

It was Paul's second day of training and today he and Trent would be working together for the first time. As Devon handed the harness to Paul, it still felt new – strange and unusual in his hands.

For years Paul had had mobility problems and relied on assistance from other people in order to get around. He used a long cane, but not confidently. As a result he rarely went out by himself. Now, suddenly, Paul's life was about to change. He felt apprehensive about it, but also quite excited; as though a door was finally opening for him. Before he could go through it, he knew he had a lot of work to do.

He and Trent began with a short walk together. It wasn't far, but for Paul it felt like miles. Somehow he had to put his faith in this dog he barely knew. He had to trust that Trent would keep him safe. That he'd stop at kerbstones and not just walk straight out on to the roads. That he'd avoid obstacles and prevent Paul from walking into things like pillar boxes, shop signs or litter bins. He had to believe that Trent would escort him carefully around other pedestrians too, weaving in and out of mums with buggies or people in mobility scooters. On top of all of that Paul had to trust that Trent would ignore all the common dog distractions: discarded food, other dogs out for a walk, or people making a fuss of him while he was working. It was a tall order!

Paul had been blind since birth and getting

around had always been a struggle for him. Now, suddenly, he had to put all his faith and his personal safety in the hands, or paws, of this dog.

It was every bit as hard as Paul imagined. For a start, Trent walked quite fast, much faster than Paul was used to walking with a cane. He struggled to keep up with the dog, and as a result lost track of where he was.

'Try and relax, Paul,' said Devon calmly. She was walking next to them, making sure Paul was safe. 'You're doing brilliantly. You've just got to trust Trent. He's a good dog. He won't let you down.'

That was the hardest part. No matter how many times someone told you the dog would keep you safe, until you'd experienced it for yourself a few times, it was impossible to believe.

Eventually Trent and Paul reached the end of

their first walk. Paul was weary. He felt light-headed from concentrating so hard and wished he was back home, relaxing in his living room. Instead, he had to turn around and do it all again on the walk back home. If it hadn't been for the support of Devon, Paul wasn't sure he'd have carried on. She was a lovely person; calm and encouraging – the ideal instructor. She smiled a lot and although she had no sight loss herself, she seemed to understand instinctively how Paul felt. She also had complete faith in him. 'You *can* do this,' she said later, as they finally arrived back at Paul's home. 'You just have to believe in yourself. I know you can do it.'

Paul wasn't so sure. He didn't say anything to Emily, of course. He didn't want to worry her. She already loved Trent to bits – as soon as she got home from school the pair would tear around the house and garden, just like any other child and their dog. But Trent wasn't their dog yet, and he wouldn't be, unless Paul qualified successfully as a guide dog owner.

'I just don't think I can do it, Trent,' he told the dog, as he turned off the lights and headed for bed that night. It was the end of the first week, and Paul felt tired and disheartened. 'How am I going to tell Emily?'

Devon wasn't about to let Paul quit. She turned up on Monday morning, as cheerful as ever, ready to repeat everything they'd done before. As far as she was concerned, she'd be there with Paul for several hours every day until he eventually mastered the techniques he needed. She would make this partnership work if it killed her!

She had her work cut out. There was so much to learn. Every signal, gesture or command had to be accurate. If Paul got it wrong, so did Trent. A wrong command could put both their lives at risk.

'It's a bit like flying a plane,' she told Paul as they set out for a walk one cold December morning. 'Think of Trent as the pilot and you as the navigator.'

Navigation was no easy matter for Paul. Crossing roads was particularly challenging. Just like all guide dogs, Trent was trained to stop at the kerb and wait until his owner gave the command 'Forward' before carrying on. It was up to Paul to decide when to cross and not Trent – although he was trained to ignore a 'Forward' command if traffic suddenly started appearing. Paul, as the guide dog owner, had to take responsibility for that too. It was the same when Paul wanted to turn left or right. He had to make that decision and tell the dog.

For Paul that was particularly hard. He had no sense of direction. He also felt he lacked the ability to feel the environment around him. He didn't know the way around his home town; he'd always relied on other people to take him where he wanted to go. Suddenly, he was not only having to get used to controlling a guide dog, but also having to remember where everything was. Paul felt as though there was little or no time to think about the route. The dog needed instructions immediately. But as Paul found himself lost again, he began to feel frustrated and fed up. He knew he probably wasn't the easiest person to train with, but Devon was unswerving in her support and encouragement. As far as she was concerned they were going to crack it. It was not a matter of *if,* but *when.*

As January turned into February things suddenly started to click for Paul. This was due, in part, to him starting to use a new satellite-navigation system on his mobile phone, which gave directions and helped him stay on track. Knowing he was following the route correctly gave Paul much more confidence in himself. He still had a few minor hiccups but one of his main routes – the walk from his home to a local cafe in town – became much easier for him.

Devon could see it happening. She could feel Paul's confidence growing every time they did the route. He looked comfortable walking at Trent's pace. He knew where he was at all times, knew when he had to cross the road and coped well in amongst the hustle and bustle of the shops in the high street. Paul and Trent finally looked safe together as a team. There were still the occasional wobbles – usually when someone stopped them to make a fuss of Trent or to chat to Paul. Apart from these minor distractions, they were working together well. Devon told Paul he was almost there, though, as always, he didn't really believe her. Then, one Friday in February, it happened.

It was a lovely day; the sun had finally made an appearance and Paul and Trent were returning home from their latest trip to town. Devon was watching from afar, hiding behind bushes and in shop doorways, keeping out of sight, but still observing them together. She was keen to see how they dealt with difficult situations or problems that arose on their walk. Then, just as they reached Paul's front door, she reappeared.

'You've done it, Paul.'

'What did you say?'

'You've qualified to walk this route by yourself with Trent.'

Paul felt a tightening in his stomach. 'Are you serious?'

'Yes, you've done it!'

Paul felt a buzz of excitement. He reached

down and tickled Trent's ears. 'We've done it, boy – we've actually done it!' Then he turned back to Devon – 'Thank you, I honestly couldn't have done it without you.' He meant it too. He grinned at Devon and said, 'I can't wait to tell Emily we can keep Trent . . . she'll be so happy!'

And she was.

Of course, Paul and Trent still had a lot of work to do. They had mastered one route – a twenty-minute trip from Paul's house into the centre of town – but there were lots of other routes Paul wanted to have a go at too. Now he knew he could do it, he was keen to venture out further. Devon would continue to help and support them all the way, delighted that Paul had finally found his independence. That was why she did the job – seeing the difference a guide dog could make to someone's life. It changed them forever. It certainly had for

Paul – for the first time in his life, he could go shopping by himself. If he ran out of milk, he could pop out and pick up a pint from his corner shop. People with sight take that sort of trip for granted, but for Paul it was a huge step and only possible with the help of a shaggy-coated big-hearted black retriever called Trent.

Several months later . . .

Paul took a deep breath. He hadn't expected to feel this nervous. His lips were dry. His hands were shaking slightly. There was a knot in his stomach.

'Hello . . . my name is Paul – I'm Emily's dad – and this is my guide dog Trent.'

He could feel all eyes on him: more than a hundred children and their teachers were sitting in the school hall, all watching and listening to his every word. Right in the middle was his daughter Emily, bursting with pride for her dad.

Paul cleared his throat. 'I'm here today to tell you all about Trent . . .' He reached down and stroked the dog's head and instantly heard his tail wagging. Paul started to relax. 'As you can see, Trent is my guide dog, and he's been with me for almost a year now. He helps me a lot. He gives me the independence and confidence to go out by myself, but getting him was hard. You see, it's not only the dogs that have to be trained to a very high standard – so do the owners.' He smiled down at Trent. They'd been through a lot together. Training to become a guide dog owner had been one of the toughest challenges of Paul's life, but now he had him, it was hard to remember life without him.

Guide Dogs

Guide dogs were first used in Germany to help soldiers who'd lost their sight during the First World War. In 1931 the first British guide dogs completed their training and three years later the charity Guide Dogs was launched. Since then they've helped thousands of blind and partially sighted people regain their mobility and independence through the guide dog service and other mobility services. There are currently 4,500 working guide dogs in the UK. The guide dog service relies entirely on voluntary donations so without your support none of this would be possible. For more information about how you can get involved with Guide Dogs visit www.guidedogs.org.uk

Puppy Days

More than a thousand guide dog puppies are currently born every year. And that number is set to grow! Guide Dogs is about to open a new national breeding centre, and once it's up and running you'll be able to visit and find out all about our puppies: how they are born, what dogs we choose, and how they take their first steps on their journey to becoming guide dogs.

The most common breed of dog we use is a Labrador and golden retriever cross-breed. But we use other types too. Here's the list:

Labrador and golden retriever cross (47%)
Labrador (31%)
Golden retriever (9%)
German shepherd (7%)
Golden retriever and German shepherd cross (3%)

The final 3% is made up of other breeds and crosses, including Labrador cross poodles and Spinones.

Puppy Names

Every litter of guide dog puppies is named after a letter of the alphabet. For example, Archie was from an 'A' litter – so all his brothers and sisters have names beginning with 'A'.

Not all of our puppies are named this way – we also invite sponsors to name puppies through our 'Name a Puppy' sponsorship scheme. This means you can fund-raise to name a puppy whatever you like (within reason!) The names need to be two syllables long and shouldn't sound like any of commands used, or be anything that a guide dog owner wouldn't feel comfortable calling out in public. Go to www.guidedogs.org.uk to find out more.

Training

Puppy Walking

Guide dog puppies start their training at around six to eight weeks old. For the first year of their life, they live with a person called a puppy walker. These are unpaid volunteers who teach our puppies all the basics they need to know: toilet training, obedience, how to walk nicely on a lead and return when they are called. The puppy walker also introduces them to all sorts of new experiences: family life, loud noises, shops, traffic, travelling, children, crowds . . . So that by the time they move onto their next stage of training, nothing should worry the pup.

Guide Dog Training

Puppy walking ends when our dogs are around twelve to fourteen months old. Now it's time for them to leave their puppy walkers and move on to their new home – working with a guide dog trainer. This is when our pups learn all the essential skills they'll need when they start work: how to cross roads safely, including always stopping at a kerb and waiting for instruction; how to avoid obstacles and safely steer their owners around anything dangerous; and how to wear the guide dog harness that their owner will hold when they are working.

Advanced Training

After about five months of guide dog training, our dogs move onto their advanced training, which takes about ten weeks. This is when they are matched up with an owner – and their trainer teaches them the specific skills that their owner will need them to know. For example, if their new owner spends a lot of time travelling on buses or trains, then their dog will get lots of practice in how to cope in that environment.

Finally the dog and its new owner spend a few weeks or months training together – getting to know one another, and the routes they will be travelling – and building a strong partnership.

Dogs are just like people: some take longer to train than others. But, generally, a guide dog is ready to start work when they're around two years old.

How Much a Guide Dog Costs

It takes a lot of time and effort to train a guide dog. We also need to feed and care for our dogs and look after the 'mum' and 'dad' dogs who have the guide dog puppies.

The lifetime cost of a guide dog (from birth to retirement) is £48,500. Here's how it all adds up:

£2,100 to breed a guide dog puppy.

£4,900 for the puppy training stage

£14,400 for guide dog training

£12,500 for advanced guide dog training

£3,500 for partnership training (when a guide dog is matched to an owner)

£11,100 to support the 'running' costs of a guide dog partnership

Guide dog owners don't have to pay for their dogs; all we ask is a nominal fee of fifty pence. When we give a dog to an owner we guarantee to support and care for that dog until they retire. We also make a lifetime commitment to the owner that we will provide them with a guide dog for as long as it can help their mobility — some owners have eight guide dogs in their lifetime! Many owners contribute to the cost of the vet's bills and their dog's food. But if they can't afford it, we will support them.

Other Careers for Our Dogs

Not all our puppies go on to become guide dogs. When they start their training we sometimes find some dogs don't have all the skills necessary. But that's not the end of their careers — many will go on to become working dogs with the police, or search-and-rescue dogs. Others will work for charities like Medical Detection Dogs or Hearing Dogs for the Deaf.

How You Can Help

There are lots of ways you can get involved in fundraising for Guide Dogs – maybe you and your class could hold a 'Get together for Guide Dogs' or go to one of our 'Go walkies for Guide Dogs' sponsored walks! You can invite a Guide Dogs speaker to come and tell your school all about what we do. They might even bring a guide dog in to meet you!

Go to www.guidedogs.org.uk to find out more.

'Sponsor a Puppy' Scheme

Guide Dogs' 'Sponsor a Puppy' scheme gives you the chance to share a puppy's journey from a cute bundle of fun to a life-changing guide dog. If you do sponsor a puppy, you'll receive regular 'pupdates' telling you how your pup is getting on, photos and a calendar featuring guide dog puppies. Go to www.sponsorapuppy.org.uk to find out more.

Dog Jokes

What is a dog's favourite cinema snack?
Pupcorn.

What is a vampire's favourite dog?
A bloodhound.

What do you call a dog that looks through keyholes?
A nosy-barker.

What do you get if you cross a spaniel, a poodle and a rooster?
A Cock-a-poodle-doo!

What does a dog like to read?
Wag azines.

What do you call a puppy sitting in a deckchair wearing sunglasses?
A hot dog.

Who is the world's most famous dog detective?
Sherlock Bones.

What is a dog's favourite vegetable?
Collie-flower.

Acknowledgements

A huge thank you to the staff and volunteers of Guide Dogs for all their help with this book, especially Lorna Catling and Ellie Gray.

And special thanks to the owners, their families and friends, and the trainers of the unforgettable dogs whose stories are shared in this book.

Archie The Howells family: Kim, Paul, Kate, Mark and Sean

Arthur Dawn and Ian Norman; Heather and Philip Brennan; Logan Anderson; Iain McLachlan

Cara Andrea Cooper

Gus Jemma Brown

Jamie Sidney Tambin

Josie The Dowling family: Lynne, Neil, Emma and Elliot

Raffles Lee and Lisa Greatbatch; Harrison and Paul Keasey

Rags The pupils and staff of RNIB Pears Centre for Specialist Learning (formerly known as RNIB Rushton School and Children's Home); Fabian and Jacqui O'Neale; Karen Gannon (RNIB Pears Centre); Louise Ashton (RNIB Pears Centre); Alfie Wilson (RNIB Pears Centre)

Shirley Rebecca and Claire Farrar; Claire Guest of Medical Detection Dogs

Trent Paul and Emily Cutress; Devon Gidley

To find out more about medical-alert dogs, see the website: www.medicaldetectiondogs.org.uk